CONTENTS

Health and Social Care for Foundation GNVQ

H O W   T O   U S E   T H I S   B O O K

Health and Social Care for Foundation GNVQ will help you prepare for this, your first GNVQ course. Each chapter has been written to cover one of the units of the course.

The first three chapters are for each of the three mandatory units, which you must take, and for which there is a test. These chapters include plenty of self-test questions, so that you can keep track of your learning as you proceed through the unit. By the time you take the test, you can be confident that you know *all* you need to know! There are also many activities, which are designed to help you gather and present the information you need for your portfolio of evidence.

The next six chapters cover the major option units of the Foundation course. You must take three of these, and will probably be told as a group which three these will be. Again there are self-test questions to check your own progress (though no test to pass!) and activities to help build your portfolio of evidence.

The activities are designed especially to develop your *key skills*. It will be important to keep a record of the key skills you have used, as you will also need to present this record with your portfolio.

The questions and activities are highlighted with icons:

 Student activity

 Self-check questions

There are other symbols throughout the book which will draw your attention to key points and useful information.

The Foundation course is designed to lead you into the field of Health and Social Care, so that you can gradually build up your knowledge and abilities. In the same way, this book increases its depth and coverage as it progresses, so that some of the later chapters will develop and extend your skills far more than the earlier ones.

Acknowledgements

The publishers would like to thank the following contributors for the permission to reproduce copyright material: fig 15, Kellogg Company; fig 16, Brian Shuel/Collections; figs 23, 25 and 43 Anthea Sieveking/ Collections; fig 32, John & Eliza Forder/ Collections; fig 22 Nancy Durrell McKenna/ The Hutchinson Library; fig 41, Nancy Fyson/J. Allan Cash Ltd; figs 75, 27, Sam Tanner/Photofusion; figs 76, 73, David Montford/Photofusion; fig 85, Comstock Photofile Ltd; fig 18, Emma Lee/Life File; fig 67, Pete Jenkins/J. Allan Cash Ltd; fig 78, J.Allan Cash Ltd; fig 10, Life File; figs 2, 3, 4, 6, 9, 13, 31, 44, 56, Science Photo Library; figs 8, 12, 30, 45, Photofusion; figs 29, 33, 34, 37, 40, Format; figs 69, 71, Action Plus.

Every effort has been made to trace copyright holders of material reproduce in this book. Any rights not acknowledged here will be acknowledged in subsequent printings if notice is given to the publisher.

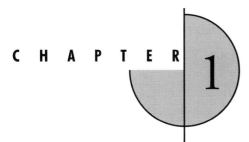

1

Investigating Health and Social Care

CONTENTS AND LINKS

This chapter will help you to find out about different kinds of health and care services available all over the country, and near where you live. You will also find out about how people use the different services, and the jobs of the people who work in them. There are many different types of health and social care service, with most of the health services being a part of the National Health Service (NHS). The social care services are either a part of the Local Authority (which is the town or county where you live), or provided by voluntary organisations which may be either national or local.

You will also find out about the jobs people do in these organisations, especially those jobs directly looking after other people. The values you are expected to follow when you are looking after other people will also be discussed.

THE MAIN TYPES OF SERVICE

Health and social care services can be put under four main headings:

- health services
- personal social services
- support groups and voluntary groups
- early years education services.

Health Services

The obvious things to put at the top of the list are the hospitals, because they are usually big places that everybody knows about. Other health services are part of everyday life, and most people have contact with them regularly yet don't think about it much. Everybody has contact with the health service at some time during their lives.

Health Services include:

- Hospitals
- The Doctors surgery (General Practitioner, GP)
- The Chemist shop (Pharmacy)

- Opticians (or Optometrist)
- Chiropodists (Podiatrists)
- Health Centres.

Personal Social Services

These are provided mainly by the Local Authorities. These are the town or countries where you live, e.g. Manchester City Council; Leicestershire County Council; Camden Borough Council, and so on.

The Social Services Department arranges most of the services. Some they will also provide, but others they will buy in from private companies and voluntary organisations.

These services include Home Care, Meals on Wheels, equipment for disabled people, day centres, old people's homes, laundry services, transport, foster care, children's homes, and social work assessment services.

When people have enough money, they can buy many of these services without going to Social Services. There are many agencies which will provide home care – chemist's shops sell equipment for disabled people; laundry services and taxis can be found just about anywhere.

Personal services such as counselling can be bought privately, and Advice and Guidance in many areas obtained free from the Citizens Advice Bureaux or other voluntary organisations.

Other personal social services are accessed through the Local Authority Housing Departments, especially for sheltered housing or housing adapted for disabled people either of these can also be paid for privately or accessed through Housing Associations.

Housing Departments often also have Housing Welfare advisers, and sometimes conciliation services to help with disputes between neighbours.

Local Authority Education Departments may have an Education Welfare Service, which deals with school refusals and truancy (bunking off).

The Environmental Health Department deals with problems of public health and hygiene and noise pollution.

Support groups and voluntary organisations

Support groups and voluntary organisations are known as 'charities'. They are not a part of either local government or central government provision, and are not private organisations, as they are not allowed to make any profits. All the money they get is used to provide services for people in need.

There are two kinds of voluntary organisation, **national** and **local**. National organisations have offices and provide a service all over the country. They include well-known names such as the NSPCC (National Society for the Prevention of Cruelty to Children), the Samaritans, Childline, RNIB (Royal National Institute for the Blind) and the Red Cross.

Local groups often have the name of the area that they cover included in their name, e.g. The Blackbury Old People Club, or the Tyneton Disabled Children's Support Group. Other examples are a hospital League of Friends who help out at only one hospital, or a Women's Refuge with a safe house in one town only.

There is usually a sort of local club where information on all these charities and support groups can be found. It is often called the Council of Voluntary Service (CVS) or the Council of Social Services (CSS). The Telephone Directory will help you to find it (look under the name of the town, e.g. Wexford CVS), or ask at the library.

Support groups are formed by people with an interest in the same things, e.g. Alcoholics Anonymous, the Motor Neurone Disease Society, Haemophilia Society, and so on. Almost all the major diseases and disabilities have an organisation providing information and support to sufferers.

Early Years Education Services

This is the name now given to all the pre-school groups that look after children up to 4 or 5 years old, when they start at primary school.

They include nurseries, crèches, childminders and playgroups as well as primary schools.

Some organisations may appear in more than one group, e.g. a voluntary organisation may provide early years education services, or a

health service may include personal social services, e.g. for people with learning difficulties.

Portfolio evidence

- As a brainstorming exercise involving everybody in the class, decide what you want to call 'local'. This may be easy, but it can be difficult to decide.
- Are you going to have all the area around the school or college, or around where you live?
- If you are in a big town, then almost everything will be within easy reach. If you are in a small town or a village, you may have to travel a lot further, and so 'local' covers a larger area.
- Where do people go for specialist services? If it is a long way away does it still class as 'local' because everybody who has a mental

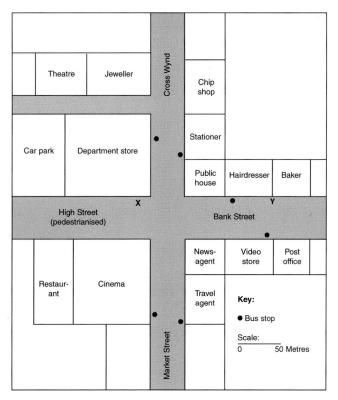

Figure 1   *A plan of part of a town centre*

illness must go to that psychiatric unit? Or everybody with burns to that Burns Unit?

- At the end of the exercise you should have decided what you want to include in your 'local' area.
- Find, or make a map of that area (Figure 1).
- Next, pick out six different organisations in your local area, making sure that there is at least one from each of the headings above (health services, personal social services, support groups and voluntary groups, and early years education services).
- If there are enough people in the class, then this can be done in small groups, with each group choosing different organisations.
- The information can be put together using information that people know and can remember – where is the chemist? Where is the doctor?, or from local directories and the telephone book, particularly Thomsons or Yellow Pages which have listings under Doctors, Pharmacies, Residential Homes, and so on. The Internet may also be a useful resource to use.
- When each group has found the information (there may only be one group, of course), they should mark on the map where all the places can be found.
- Make sure that the map is kept safe, with a copy for everybody's portfolio, and move on to the next piece of work.

MAIN JOBS IN HEALTH AND SOCIAL CARE SERVICES

The jobs we most often think of in caring are those where somebody is directly looking after the needs of another person, such as doctors, nurses and care assistants. These workers are known as '**direct carers**', as they look after patients and clients directly.

Another group of people who also do this are known as '**informal carers**'. The difference between them and direct carers is that informal carers are not paid any wages. They are usually the relatives, friends and neighbours of the people who need looking after.

The third group of workers essential to care are the '**indirect carers**'. They are the people who do the work which supports the direct carers, such as the cooks, porters, domestic staff and office workers.

Doctors

Simon's training to become a doctor took seven years. After his training finished and he passed his exams, Simon had to get experience in different kinds of medicine before picking the job he wanted to do. That meant specialising in one kind of work.

Most doctors work for the National Health Service, although there are some who work only with private patients. Some doctors work in specific settings, for example Occupational Health Physicians work in industrial places such as factories, mines or offices. Others choose to work in the Army or the Navy.

Quite a lot want to be family doctors, also known as General Practitioners (or GPs). They are said to be in General Practice

Figure 2   *'Simon'*

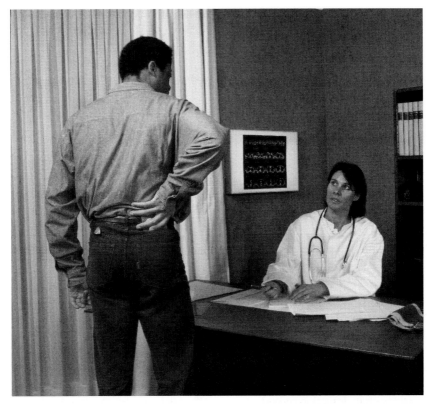

Figure 3   *GP with patient*

because they deal with everything that can go wrong with people. Patients either turn up at the surgery or call the doctor out whenever they are ill or injured. So family doctors deal with the general mixture of things that can go wrong with people.

General Practitioners are different to doctors who work in hospitals, who are specialists in certain kinds of work.

A GP will send (or 'refer') people to a specialist for advice or another opinion on something that he or she is not certain about, or for treatment that cannot be given at home or in the surgery or Health Centre.

A specialist is someone like a surgeon who will do an operation, or a cancer specialist who will arrange radiation treatment.

They may also be Psychiatrists, who deal with mental illness, or dermatologists who treat skin diseases. There are many more specialists, some you may have heard of and some you may not. A couple of the more common ones are Paediatricians, specialising in the treatment of children, and Geriatricians, dealing with the problems of old age. More and more doctors are now working in Health Centres, sharing with other doctors and people from other caring professions (such as nurses, Health Visitors and Midwives).

The first person you will meet is the Receptionist, who is an indirect carer, and who will be responsible for taking your name and address, making an appointment for you, and then finding your medical records to give to the doctor when you arrive for the appointment.

Figure 4   *A busy Health Centre*

Self-check questions

- What do the initials GP stand for?
- When a GP 'refers' a patient to a specialist, what does this mean?
- Why are Family Doctors also called General Practitioners?
- What is the name given to a doctor who specialises in the treatment of children?
- What sort of people does a Geriatrician look after?
- Name two caring professions working in Health Centres.
- What does the Receptionist at a Health Centre do?

Student key skills activity

- Make some record cards like the one pictured here. Fill it in for yourself, and use them in the next exercise. This will help toward achieving key skills in Communications.
- Make up a short play about going to see the doctor at a Health Centre. Somebody will have to pretend to be the doctor, and other

people will play the receptionist and the patient.

- It is best to do this in small groups; not everyone has to act a part, but everyone should help with the planning.
- Each group should have a different role play to the other groups.
- You could start with the patient going to the receptionist and asking to see the doctor. The receptionist will then say that the patient has to have an appointment, and ask questions about name, address, and what is wrong. The record card will then have to be found from the ones you filled in before.

Surname
1st names
Date of birth
Address
Doctor
Previous visit
Special notes
Medical No.

Figure 5   *A simple record card*

- The patient could then argue that they want to see the doctor straight away, because it is urgent. Decide in your group if anyone is going to pretend to be angry, or just do as they are told.
- The next scene is with the patient seeing the doctor. Work out in your group what you think the doctor and the patient will say to each other.
- Afterwards, the other groups should say what they thought of the play.
- Is what happens when you go to the doctor?
- For the 'actors', what was it like to be a doctor or receptionist or patient?

Nurses

Martin trained as a general nurse; the qualification he got is RGN, which stands for Registered General Nurse. The course was three years long. He went to a college, and on placements with qualified nurses in hospitals and in the community, and had to pass exams.

There are three other types of nurse training besides the RGN, all of them taking three years of study.

One is working with mentally ill people; this is the Registered Mental Nurse (RMN). Another is the Registered Sick Childrens' Nurse (RSCN), and the last is the Registered Nurse for the Mentally Handicapped (RNMH).

When they are qualified, most nurses work in hospitals, but there are many other things they can go on to do. Some of these other jobs mean that they have to do more training, for example if they want to be a **Midwife** or a **Health Visitor**. Sometimes it is where they work and the kind of work they do which gives nurses a slightly different title. It is also possible to train as a Midwife at some Colleges of Nursing without training to be a nurse first.

Practice nurses work in the surgery or Health Centre and do some of the work for the doctors, and also give some treatments which may otherwise have to be done in hospitals.

The nurses will do things like taking blood pressure and testing urine; also giving advice on diets and how to look after sick people.

Figure 6   *Male Nurse, 'Martin'*

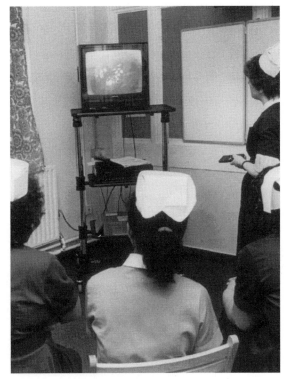

Figure 7   *Nurses study for three years*

Practice Nurses also give treatments such as injections, putting on or changing dressings, and syringing ears (washing the wax out).

District Nurses do the same kinds of things, but they go around visiting people in their own homes and give people baths or help them to the toilet as well as give injections, change dressings and so on. This is known as domiciliary visiting; a 'domicile' is where someone lives. **Health Visitors (HVs)** are nurses who have had extra training, and visit people at home to educate them about health matters. They do most of their work with families who have children under 5 years old, but they are also involved with older people and people with disabilities.

Midwives may also work from doctors surgeries and Health Centres; their job is to provide assistance and medical care to women during late pregnancy, labour and childbirth and until the children are ten days old, when the Health Visitor takes over responsibility.

Midwifery training is available to both men and women, just as nursing is.

Most nurses work for local Health Authorities and Trusts, but many work in private Nursing Homes, hospitals and residential homes. Some work for private agencies, and work in people's own homes. A few work for Voluntary organisations, such as McMillan Nurses, who look after cancer patients in the patient's own home. Other staff who work with the nurses and help them do their job are **Care Assistants**.

In hospitals, they will probably be known as Health Care Assistants; in other places such as Retirement Homes, they will be called Care Assistants. Their job is to help with the everyday things such as getting people up and dressed, bathing and washing, helping people to eat and generally keeping them happy.

Care Assistants are encouraged to do a National Vocational Qualification in Care at Level 2 or Level 3 (Level 3 is for people who supervise other workers).

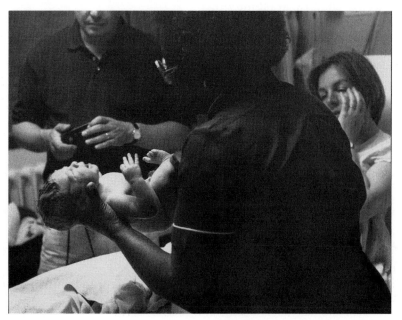

Figure 8   *A midwife at work*

Social Workers (SWs) work mainly for Social Services Departments (SSDs), but may be based at Health Centres or in hospitals as well as SSD offices. They may also be employed privately by doctors, but are more likely to be employed by the Social Services Department and go to the surgery for a few hours a week to see people the doctor thinks have social problems.

Some social workers are employed by solicitors to help with work in the law courts; others work for voluntary organisations such as the National Society for the Prevention of Cruelty to Children (NSPCC) and Childline.

Occupational Therapists can be found working in the Health Service and in Social Services. They are often called 'OTs', and their job is to help people manage their day to day lives in a practical way. They will advise on how to do things better if you lose an arm, for instance. They also work out the best ways to change a house to suit somebody in a wheelchair, or who uses a walking frame. People with arthritis and some other diseases can't grip properly, so the OT will help them to find the aids that they need to help get over this. These might be taps with long handles, or kettles that rock to pour the water out instead of having to be lifted up.

Indirect Carers include the Laboratory staff; when a doctor takes some blood, urine or a swab for test, it has to be sent off to a laboratory for the tests to be done. The technicians and laboratory assistants who work there will do the tests and send the results beck to the doctor.

Everybody needs to eat, so another important indirect care job is preparing and serving food; not just to the patients, but also to the care staff. Cooks, kitchen assistants, food servers, drivers and meals on wheels staff will all be involved. Meals on wheels are made in a kitchen and sent off to peoples' houses in a van with insulated containers to keep the food warm.

Figure 9   *A lab technician*

Everywhere has to be kept clean, and the people who do this are the **domestic staff**. They may be either porters or cleaners, and they are indirect care workers as well.

Nursery Nurses

When any parent with young children wants to go out to work, whether it is as a direct carer or indirect carer, they will have to have someone to look after their children. If it is not an informal carer such as a relative, friend or neighbour then it is very likely to be a Nursery Nurse.

Nursery Nurses work anywhere that children under eight are looked after. This includes nurseries, playgroups, and crèches; also in schools and on hospital wards, or possibly looking after children at home such as nannies, or as childminders.

Nursery Nurses do two years training to get the BTEC Diploma Certificate in Childhood Studies, or a CACHE Diploma in Nursery Nursing (which used to be the NNEB Diploma). They can also do a National Vocational Qualification (NVQ) in Early Years Care and Education at either Level 2 or Level 3.

Self-check questions

- Where do Practice Nurses work?
- Who do Occupational Therapists work for?
- Where do District Nurses see their patients?
- Which age group do Health Visitors do most of their work with?
- What do Midwives do?
- What training are Care Assistants encouraged to do?

- Who does the blood tests for doctors?
- Name two types of catering staff.
- Who are usually informal carers?
- What ages are the children that Nursery Nurses look after?

The care value base

This is something that all carers should know about, no matter where they are working. Everybody should be treated with respect. Look after other people as you would like to be looked after yourself, and you will be on the way to doing the right thing.

The care value base means:

- making sure that services do not discriminate unfairly
- keeping information about clients confidential
- promoting and supporting clients' rights to dignity, independence, choice, health and safety
- being sensitive to other peoples' personal beliefs
- supporting clients by using good communication skills.

Here are some examples of how this happens:

New buildings are designed so that disabled people can get in and out easily; some older buildings may have changes made to them for the same reason. Opening hours may be arranged so those people working regularly from 9 a.m. to 5 p.m. can get there (e.g. GP's evening surgeries).

When patients go in to see their doctor, they do not expect him or her to tell everything to the next person who goes in to the surgery. If you are on placement or working as a carer, you should not tell anybody private information about what has gone on with other people. It is OK to tell other people about what has happened without mentioning any names or other information which might help to identify people.

So you can tell the group in class that an old lady fell over and broke her hip when you were working at the Residential Home. but not that Mrs Smith who used to live in Devon Street has fallen and broken her hip.

Things that people tell you when you are caring for them should not be repeated outside the place that they are cared for; but you will often have to tell other people who work in the same place so that you can all do your job properly.

When carers like you are looking after other people, you should call them by the name that they like to be called. 'Granny', 'Duck' or 'Love' are only acceptable if the other person has no objections. Find out what they like to be called; is it Jen, Jenny, or Jennifer? Or would they prefer 'Mrs Dobbins' or 'Mr Clark'?

Looking after other people does not mean that you have to do everything for them. You should let people do as much as they can for themselves, even if they are very slow about it. This is encouraging independence.

Asking which clothes people would like to wear or what they would like to eat are examples of giving choices.

Being sensitive to someone else's personal beliefs most often comes up over religion and food. If someone is vegetarian or vegan, then the food that they are given should be suitable for them. People of different religions should be allowed to worship in their own way, and arrangements made so that they are able to do so. Where people speak another language, or have communication difficulties because they are deaf or have had a stroke for example, then information should be made available to them in a way that they can understand. This may be written in their own language, or through sign language for deaf people.

Questions

 1 Can you think of any more examples yourself?

2 When you are out on placements, or speaking to carers, especially professional carers, ask them for some more examples of care values in practice.

3 You could organise a role-play of someone getting up for breakfast, and try to include as many examples of care values in action as you think of.

Portfolio evidence

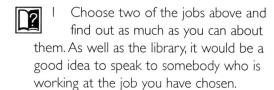 1 Choose two of the jobs above and find out as much as you can about them. As well as the library, it would be a good idea to speak to somebody who is working at the job you have chosen.

2 Find what they do when they are at work, and how they use the value base in what they do.

Inviting a speaker

- Decide who it is you would like to invite, either a person you know or somebody you do not know who is doing the job you are interested in.
- You could also invite somebody who can give advice on how to find jobs, such as a Careers Adviser.
- If you cannot think of anyone, ask your tutors for help.
- Find out from your tutors when would be the best time to ask somebody to come in

– not just the day of the week, but the best time of the day as well.

- When you have decided who it is you will be inviting, one of you will have to ring them up and ask them if they will come and talk to you. If they will, check which day they will be free, and if the time your tutor gave you is OK for them.

If they are not able to come, ask if they know anybody who can, and then speak to that person. (It is a good idea to ask now if they will want to be paid for coming to speak, and telling your tutor if they do before you do anything else.)

- When you have found somebody to come, you will have to write them a letter (using a word-processor) confirming the dates and times.
- You should also ask them if they will want anything for the talk, such as an overhead projector, or a flip-chart.

Use school or college headed paper for your letter, and have it checked by your tutor before you send it out.

- On the day of the talk, two of your group should meet your guest when they arrive, and show them to the room. You could also show them where the toilet is, and ask if they want a drink of tea or coffee. Do not forget to introduce them to your tutor.
- After the talk, remember to thank them for their time, and make sure that one of you shows them to the way out. They may not know their way around as well as you do.
- Write a letter of thanks to be sent out afterwards.
- Write about what you did to help organise the visit, and use this evidence in your log book of Key Skills.

If more than one speaker is wanted, you can do the same thing again for them, but share the work out so that everybody has a chance to take part in organising the visits.

Writing the letters for this section will give you evidence towards Key Skills in Communications, and Information Technology if you use a word-processor – don't forget to use the spellchecker!

ACCESS TO LOCAL HEALTH, SOCIAL CARE AND EARLY YEARS PROVISION

'Getting access' to services means how people can get to use them. There are different ways for different services.

Health Services

Many health services have 'direct access', which means you can just walk in off the street. This is what happens with opticians, dentists and chemists shops. With Family Doctors (General Practitioners), you have to join their list of patients, and to do this you have to live within a reasonable distance of the surgery or Health Centre. Doctors will travel a lot further in the countryside than they do in the big towns. The doctor must also be prepared to let you join the list, and his list must not be full. The government only allows doctors to have a certain number of patients on their books.

METHODS OF REFERRAL

A referral is when a health or social care agency is asked to help a client. There are three main ways that this can happen:

- a **self-referral**
- **professional referral,**
- and a **third party referral**.

A **self referral** is when you ask for help for yourself.

A **professional referral** is when you go to see your doctor, or perhaps your dentist, or a chiropodist, and they think that you need help or treatment that they cannot give. They will send you to see a consultant who specialises in what is thought to be wrong with you.

A **third party referral** is when somebody else asks for help, such as a friend, relative or neighbour.

Student exercise

Read the case studies below, and decide which type of referral each one is.

1 Mrs J. sees her neighbour have a fall in the garden, and calls an ambulance.
2 Jon has stomach ache, so goes to the doctor for help.
3 Rachel cuts her hand at work, and goes to Casualty Department for urgent treatment.
4 Jons' doctor thinks it may be appendicitis, so sends him to the hospital to see a surgeon.
5 Chris goes to the dentist, and is sent to her GP because the dentist thinks the main problem has nothing to do with her teeth.
6 Alan has an eye test, and the optician sends him to the GP as he thinks there may be an eye infection which needs treatment.
7 Sue is worried that her sister in laws children are not being looked after properly, so she rings the Social Services to tell them about it.
8 Ram wants his house altered so that he can get around it better in his wheelchair. He rings the Occupational Therapist at Social Services for an assessment.
9 The social worker thinks that Mollie is mentally ill, so asks a psychiatrist to visit and

give an opinion.
10 The Health Visitor wants to arrange care for a child when a mother is in hospital having another baby. She rings Social Services for help.
(These questions and your answers can be used as portfolio evidence.)

Possible barriers to access

The first possible barrier is the psychological one: do people realise that they need help, and are they willing to ask for it? Older people, for example, don't always accept that they can't do things for themselves anymore, and are too proud to ask for any help. Other people notice that they are not looking after themselves as well as they used to, perhaps by not eating properly, or not keeping as clean as they did. Some people are afraid of doctors or hospitals, or of having injections. They may be shy about being seen with no clothes on. All of these things have to be overcome before care can be given.

TIME

There are some health and care services which people cannot get by self referral, they have to go through a specialist. When they want to see a consultant, patients will first have to go and see their doctor and get a referral from there. If they can afford to pay, they can make a self-referral, but most people still go through their GP. For something urgent, it is sometimes possible to go to a Casualty Department and be seen there by a consultant without going to the GP first.

When a patient wants to see a GP, they will first need to know when the surgery or Health Centre is open. They will then have to make an appointment. It is not often that people can walk in to a doctors surgery and be seen quickly these days. So there are

Figure 10   *Surgery opening times*

restrictions on when people can be seen, and sometimes by whom. In the bigger Health Centres, it is often the next doctor who is available that has to be seen rather than being able to choose the doctor personally.

Some Casualty Departments are open 24 hours a day; some close at nights, and occasionally at weekends. Other services are restricted in the times that they are open, and in the times that they are available to the public. Dentists and opticians work on an appointment system, and so do many Social Services offices.

The times that different services are open can be a major barrier to the availability of their services.

You need to find out about the following in your area:

- Is the Casualty Department open all the time?
- What system do the local doctors use? Do they all use the same system for appointments or seeing people at home?
- Do people have to make an appointment to see a duty social worker?
- Can people get an eye test any time they want one?
- How long do people have to wait to see a dentist?

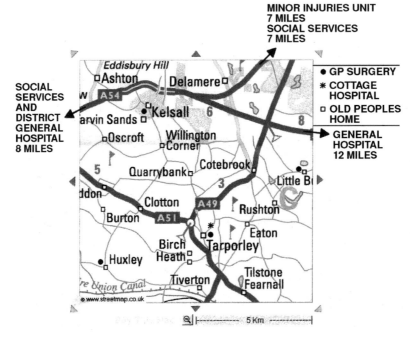

Figure 11   *Amenities in a rural area*

WHAT IS LOCAL?

How far away are all these services to where people live? Do a survey in your school or college; ask people how far they would have to travel to get to the Casualty Department or the Social Services Office: then find out how much it would cost them in bus or train fares or by taxi.

If people live in the countryside, they could be a long way from any of the health and care services which are fairly easy to reach in towns. They would have to pay a lot more to get there.

Don't forget to decide with your teacher/lecturer what you are going to include in 'local'.

PHYSICAL ACCESS

Remember that many of the people needing health and care services have trouble getting out and about. What is the entrance like at the doctor's surgery, or the Health Centre? Can mothers with prams get in easily, or people in wheelchairs? What about the Social Services Office?

Could people with wheelchairs or children in prams get inside easily? Are there any double doors, swing doors, or sharp corners to get round? The biggest restriction will be if there are steps there, or if the office people want to get to is upstairs and there is no lift, or the lift is not big enough or has other problems for disabled people. Are the floor numbers in

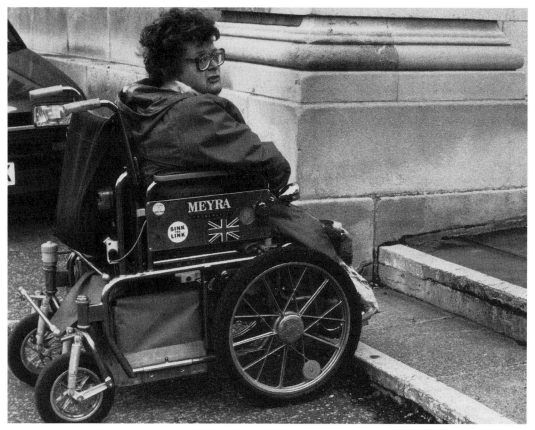

Figure 12   *A wheelchair user's experience*

Braille as well as written? Can a person in a wheelchair reach the controls – is the lift big enough to take a wheelchair and a helper?

Student activity

- Start by looking around your school or college. If you can borrow a wheelchair, so much the better. Make a tour and see where the problem areas are for wheelchair users, or other people who have difficulty walking. Draw a plan of the building you are touring, and mark on it the difficult areas. How easy is it to get into the toilets (and out again)? Is the lighting OK for people with poor eyesight?
- When you have looked at the school or college, you will have a better idea of what is needed. Go and look at the offices of the health and care services in your area, including the voluntary organisations, and see what you think of their facilities for disabled people.

Key skills exercise

1. If you had to put a ramp in to get wheelchairs in and out, what angle would be the best? If it is too steep, the user may not be strong enough to get up it; if it is too shallow, it would have to be longer and there may not be room to build it. Work the angle out for yourself and put it into your portfolio for Application of Number Key Skills.
2. Choose one of the services you have looked at, and write about how access could be improved. Remember that improving access for wheelchairs also improves access for

mothers with children in prams and pushchairs.

FINANCIAL

Do any of the services you have been looking at make a charge to the patients or clients? How much does it cost to see a doctor? Get a check-up from a dentist? Have an eye test? See a social worker?

You looked earlier at how much it costs for people to get to the various health and care services: This may put them off from using them. If they also have to pay for the service offered, that might put them off even more. How many people do you know who do not bother going to the dentist, or who do not have an eye test because it costs money?

The government also tries to save money by having specialist services in one place, and making people travel to them. We mentioned Children' Hospitals earlier. Where do people from your area have to go for kidney dialysis? Where is the nearest Burns Unit? or Premature Baby Unit? Psychiatric Department? Not all hospitals have all of these.

Key skills exercise

1. To get some more evidence of key skills, you could work out how much it would cost for people to get to their out-patient appointments using buses or taxis, or trains if it is along way to go.
2. Choose a single person, an elderly couple, and a young mother with three children under five years old.

ASSESSMENT EVIDENCE

You need to produce a report on local health and social care services. It must include:

- information about the health care, social care and early years services (health, personal social services, support and education services) in your local area

- identification of the main jobs in the services

- description of different jobs of people in these services

- description of access to the services

To achieve a pass you must show you can:	To achieve a merit you must also show you can:	To achieve a distinction you must also show you can:
• identify the main local health, social care and early years provision in your locality	• demonstrate the ability to work on your own in collecting some of the information you need	• demonstrate an understanding of the care value base by describing clearly how it is applied by workers in the health, social care and early years services
• clearly locate these services on a map of the area	• accurately describe the principles of the care value base	
• give basic descriptions of job roles in each of the services	• clearly explain the barriers that people might have to overcome to gain access to services	• give relevant examples of what the services could do to overcome the barriers
• describe two ways in which people are referred to the health, social care and early years providers shown on the map		

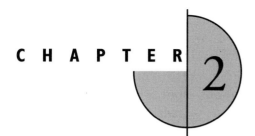

CHAPTER 2

Understanding health and well-being

CONTENTS AND LINKS

This unit links with Foundation Unit 3 (Understanding personal development and relationships), Unit 5 (Planning diets) and Unit 4 (Investigating common hazards and health emergencies). It will also prepare you for Intermediate Unit 2 (Promoting health and well-being).

If you are thinking about a job looking after other people, it is important to know how to keep them and yourself as fit and well as possible – both physically and mentally.

WHAT DO WE MEAN BY HEALTH AND WELL-BEING?

Health and well-being is feeling fine and looking good, being fit and not having any illnesses. It also involves having positive relationships with other people, – family, friends, other students and staff at school and college, work or anywhere else.

There are four parts to health and well-being, and these are:

- *Physical aspects* – how your body grows and changes, and what it need to be able to do this.

- *Intellectual aspects* – how the mind develops continuously. This is helped by playing games, watching TV, reading and so on.
- *Emotional aspects* – learning about our feelings and growing more confident.
- *Social aspects* – learning how to live with, get along with and work with other people.

You may have noticed that the first letter of each of these aspects spells PIES. Think of apple pies or mince pies. This will make it easier to remember, and PIES are an important part of Health and Social Care. You will be using PIES a lot on this course (see page 41).

Health and well-being are different at different ages, so what is important for a baby will not be so important to a teenager.

The main life stages are:

- Infants (0–3)
- Young children (4–9)
- Adolescents (10–18)
- Adults (19–65)
- Elderly people (65+)

Different books may give you slightly different ages for these stages, but they should all be roughly the same. There may also be different divisions, such as Young Adults, and Middle Age. Don't worry about it, you will be able to work out where these fit on the list above. If you can't then ask the teacher.

There is more information on these life stages in Unit 3 (Chapter 3 in this book, pages 38–64).

FACTORS AFFECTING HEALTH AND WELL-BEING

There are many things in our lives which affect us. These include the things that we eat, what we do with our spare time such as exercise (dancing, playing football, swimming, and so on), or going out drinking, smoking, or taking drugs. Even the place where you live can make a difference. Do you live at the top of a large block of flats, or is your house near a factory making chemicals and where the air has a funny smell all the time? Or are you out in the countryside with no neighbours for miles? It also makes a difference if people have jobs, and those who have more money are usually also healthy and happier with life (but this is not always true).

As you will have noticed by now, not everyone is the same. Some of the differences are physical – some of us are fat, some are thin, some are short and some are tall. Diet is one of the factors influencing this.

DIET

This is the word for all the things we eat and drink. When people talk about 'dieting' or being on a 'special diet', they mean that they are taking care about what they eat, and choosing their food and drinks carefully. This will be to make sure that they get all the nutrients their body needs, or to avoid anything which may do harm or disagree with them. So people who are slimming will try to avoid any foods or drinks with a lot of sugar or fats in them, and pregnant women will want to get as much iron and vitamins into their diet as possible.

If you are eating normally, it is not necessary to do any more than make sure that you are getting a good mix of foods to make up a 'balanced diet'. If you want to eat chocolate or drink cola, this is fine – so long as it is not too much, and part of an overall healthy diet.

The more you eat different kinds of food, the more chance you have of getting something of everything you need to be healthy.

SO WHAT DO WE NEED TO PUT INTO A BALANCED HEALTHY DIET?

Protein: this comes from eating meat, fish, cheese and eggs, as well as peas, beans, lentils and nuts.

Fats from butter, margarine, milk, cheese, fat in meat, and cooking oils.

Carbohydrates from bread, pasta, rice and cereals; and

Figure 13   *Healthy eating*

Fibre, which is found in fruit and vegetables as well as some breakfast cereals.

If you are eating a balanced diet, some foods from each section should be included every day. All the main supermarkets have leaflets and booklets available to give advice on healthy eating, and they are given away free.

You can also get lots of information from the Health Education Authority, or the Health Education Unit of your local Health Trust. Their number and address will be in your local phone book.

There is often useful information on food packaging.

The questionnaire on page 22 was on Kelloggs All-Bran boxes a little while ago.

Should we be worried?

By the time we are adults most of us will suffer some form of disease due to our diet. We only have to look in our mouths to see fillings. A trivial disease, perhaps, but dental

Figure 14   *A supermarket leaflet*

services cost the National Health Service (NHS) over £450 million every year. If we could look at our hearts and arteries and see their condition we might be more alarmed. Heart disease kills a quarter of us, and what we eat contributes greatly to these deaths.

Worse still, the age at which heart disease occurs is decreasing – people in their 30s and 40's are having heart attacks in increasing numbers. Cancer, too, is often related to diet. A report from the World Health Organisation estimated that about 40% of cancers in men, and a remarkable 60% in women were linked to diets that had too much fatty foods – especially animal fats – and not enough vegetables and fruit. Apart from the links between smoking and lung cancer, diet was the main cause of cancer, especially of the mouth, stomach and bowel, as well as of the breast and womb. Piles (haemorrhoids) and various other bowel diseases occurring in later life are often the result of a lifetime of eating low-fibre food.

Other diseases are related to eating too much and becoming overweight. From cancer to coronaries, skin disorders to constipation, diet is being recognised as a major factor in our general health.

(Reproduced from *the Nursery Food Book* by M. Whiting and T. Lobstein, published by Edward Arnold)

Self-check questions

- What will most of us have suffered by the time we are adults?
- How much do dental services cost each year?
- How many of us does heart disease kill?
- What is happening to the age at which heart disease occurs?

- What is cancer related to?
- What % of cancers in women are linked to too much fatty food?
- What is strongly linked with lung cancer?
- What is often the result of eating low fibre food?

Risks

What can go wrong if people do not have a balanced diet?

Find out about vitamin deficiencies and mineral deficiencies such as anaemia.

What can you find out about anorexia and bulimia?

What problems may people have if they are too fat?

A lot more information on diets and food can be found in Unit 5, Chapter 5 of this book (pages 97–117).

PERSONAL HYGIENE

A very important way to look after yourself and other people is to make sure that both you and they are as clean and hygienic as possible. Personal hygiene may not seem that important until somebody tells you that you are smelly. If you do not keep your body clean you can get skin infections and diseases, mouth problems, and little animals which live in your hair and skin such as lice and scabies.

Being clean and tidy is even more important when you are looking after other people. You have to get very close to them sometimes, when you are feeding or lifting people, for example. Not very nice for them if you have smelly armpits and bad breath, is it?

How much fibre do you eat?

Most people know fibre is important but, despite this, research shows that nine out of every ten people are still not eating enough fibre—are you?

QUESTIONNAIRE

To help you find out how much fibre you eat, Kellogg's has obtained a simple self-analysed questionnaire. Devised and tested by the University of Birmingham Department of Social Medicine, the questionnaire will enable you to analyse your diet for fibre intake. It's simple to fill in and there are no right or wrong answers, so be honest with yourself!

HOW TO COMPLETE

Answer each question. Tick the box nearest to your answer, e.g. Question 1, if your answer is D—tick score 20.

1 What kind of breakfast cereal do you regularly eat?

		SCORE
A.	All Bran, other high fibre cereal	A. 100
B.	Puffed wheat, bran flakes, wheat biscuits, shredded wheat, wheat flakes, other whole wheat cereal, oat bran flakes	B. 50
C.	Muesli	C. 50
D.	Corn flakes, Rice Krispies, other cereal	D. 20
E.	Don't eat breakfast cereal	E. 0

2 On a typical weekday, how many slices of bread do you eat? (a roll counts as two slices of bread)

		SCORE
A.	None	A. 0
B.	1–2	B. 28
C.	3–5	C. 56
D.	6 or more	D. 84

3 What sort of bread do you usually eat?

		SCORE
A.	Wholemeal	A. 20
B.	Brown (not wholemeal)	B. 7
C.	White	C. 5
D.	Mixture of bread types	D. 7
E.	None	E. 0

4 On a typical weekday, how many biscuits would you eat?

		SCORE
A.	5 or more	A. 6
B.	3 or 4	B. 4
C.	1 or 2	C. 2
D.	Only eat biscuits once or twice in a week	D. 1
E.	Rarely or never eat biscuits	E. 0

The following answers refer to questions 5–22

How many times a week do you eat these foods?

A. Twice or more a day
B. Once a day
C. 5–6 times a week
D. 3–4 times a week
E. Twice a week
F. Once a week
G. Once a fortnight
H. Less than once a fortnight

5 Baked beans:

	SCORE		SCORE		SCORE		SCORE
A.	140	B.	70	C.	50	D.	30
E.	20	F.	10	G.	5	H.	0

6 Breakfast cereal:

	SCORE		SCORE		SCORE		SCORE
A.	112	B.	56	C.	40	D.	24
E.	16	F.	8	G.	4	H.	0

7 Fresh fruit:

	SCORE		SCORE		SCORE		SCORE
A.	70	B.	35	C.	25	D.	15
E.	10	F.	5	G.	3	H.	0

8 Tinned fruit:

	SCORE		SCORE		SCORE		SCORE
A.	70	B.	35	C.	25	D.	15
E.	10	F.	5	G.	3	H.	0

9 Dried fruit:

	SCORE		SCORE		SCORE		SCORE
A.	70	B.	35	C.	25	D.	15
E.	10	F.	5	G.	3	H.	0

10 Leafy vegetables, e.g. cabbage:

	SCORE		SCORE		SCORE		SCORE
A.	42	B.	21	C.	15	D.	9
E.	6	F.	3	G.	2	H.	0

11 Root vegetables, e.g. carrots:

	SCORE		SCORE		SCORE		SCORE
A.	42	B.	21	C.	15	D.	9
E.	6	F.	3	G.	2	H.	0

12 Jacket potatoes:

	SCORE		SCORE		SCORE		SCORE
A.	28	B.	14	C.	10	D.	6
E.	4	F.	2	G.	1	H.	0

13 Boiled potatoes:

	SCORE		SCORE		SCORE		SCORE
A.	28	B.	14	C.	10	D.	6
E.	4	F.	2	G.	1	H.	0

14 Mashed potatoes:

	SCORE		SCORE		SCORE		SCORE
A.	28	B.	14	C.	10	D.	6
E.	4	F.	2	G.	1	H.	0

15 Roast potatoes:

	SCORE		SCORE		SCORE		SCORE
A.	28	B.	14	C.	10	D.	6
E.	4	F.	2	G.	1	H.	0

16 Chips:

	SCORE		SCORE		SCORE		SCORE
A.	28	B.	14	C.	10	D.	6
E.	4	F.	2	G.	1	H.	0

17 Biscuits:

	SCORE		SCORE		SCORE		SCORE
A.	28	B.	14	C.	10	D.	6
E.	4	F.	2	G.	1	H.	0

18 Rice:

	SCORE		SCORE		SCORE		SCORE
A.	14	B.	7	C.	5	D.	3
E.	2	F.	1	G.	1	H.	0

19 Pasta:

	SCORE		SCORE		SCORE		SCORE
A.	14	B.	7	C.	5	D.	3
E.	2	F.	1	G.	1	H.	0

20 Crispbreads:

	SCORE		SCORE		SCORE		SCORE
A.	14	B.	7	C.	5	D.	3
E.	2	F.	1	G.	1	H.	0

21 Crisps:

	SCORE		SCORE		SCORE		SCORE
A.	14	B.	7	C.	5	D.	3
E.	2	F.	1	G.	1	H.	0

22 Salads:

	SCORE		SCORE		SCORE		SCORE
A.	14	B.	7	C.	5	D.	3
E.	2	F.	1	G.	1	H.	0

THE ANALYSIS

Now add up all the scores you ticked and your total score will provide you with an indication of your fibre intake.

If it is:

Less than 170—your fibre intake is low and you are most likely to benefit by eating more fibre-rich foods.

Between 171 and 230—you are on the border line and you may wish to consider including a few more high-fibre foods in your daily diet.

Over 231—Well done, your fibre intake is adequate and meets the recommendations set by health experts. You should be enjoying all the benefits of a fibre-rich diet. Keep it up!

Kellogg's
ALL-BRAN

Figure 15   *Kellogg's questionnaire on fibre*

The mouth

It is important to keep the mouth clean and healthy. Teeth and gums need cleaning regularly followed by a mouthwash to freshen up and clean the rest of the mouth and throat. False teeth need to be taken out and cleaned regularly, as well.

Not keeping the mouth clean can lead to bad breath, gum infection (gingivitis), mouth ulcers, tooth decay and throat infections.

When people do get problems in the mouth, it can stop them eating properly, and may lead to malnutrition, deficiency diseases and possible dehydration. (If you do not understand these words, look them up in a dictionary. A medical dictionary would be very useful).

The skin

Skin need to be kept clean, and some parts of the body are more difficult to keep clean than others. Hands are normally washed many times every day; faces may also be rinsed quite frequently. Some people take baths or showers much more often than others do. When looking after people, you should find out how often they like to either take a bath or a shower, and which one they want.

Parts of the body that should be kept especially clean are under the arms, the feet, and the bottom, including the genitals.

If skin is not kept clean, it can become slippery and smelly, attracting bacteria. Infections can then develop more easily, causing itchy skin rashes. Important parts of the skin are the nose and the ears. Don't forget that these need to be kept clean as well.

Hair and nails

Hair needs to be kept clean; this is not too difficult if you can get into a bath or a shower, but can be a problem for people who have to stay in bed. There are many ways to do it, though, and things to help you to do it. Hair also needs to be cut sometimes. And you may have to arrange for a hairdresser to visit people. Men also need to shave; another kind of hair to look after. It is much safer to use an electric razor to do this. Finger nails and toenails also need to be kept clean and short. Fingernails should be cut in a curve to match the finger; toenails are better cut straight, as this helps to stop people getting 'ingrowing toenails'. You may be able to cut nails yourself, but if there are problems, then a manicurist should look after the fingernails, and a chiropodist should look after the toenails.

PHYSICAL EXERCISE

Keeping healthy is not just a matter of eating a balanced diet. There are a number of other things involved, and one of these is to get enough exercise.

Exercise is also very important, and can be done whilst taking part in other recreational activities or hobbies which are a complete change from studying and work. In order to keep fit, you should do something energetic at least three times a week, and for at least twenty minutes each time.

Exercise helps to improve your strength, suppleness (being able to move and bend more easily) and stamina (staying power). You should only do exercise you are able to do safely. Older people will not be able to do all the things that teenagers do, for example, and young children or disabled people will have to have exercises designed to meet their needs. There are plenty of wheelchair sports, though, including basketball and rugby!

Figure 16   *There are many ways to keep fit*

Student exercise

- Where do the people who live in your area go for their exercise? Either draw a map, or mark on a printed map, the places you have found. For example, the park, leisure centre, skating rink and swimming pool.

The non-active pastimes also have benefits for the people taking part in them. It may be something as simple as stopping them getting bored, but it may also help them learn new things, or bring them into contact with other people.

Risks

As we have explained here, exercise is good for you, but like everything else, you can have too much of a good thing.

- What can go wrong if you over-do things when you are exercising?
- What advice would be given to people with heart problems or asthma when they want to take exercise?
- Would you know how to deal with sprains, strains and broken bones?

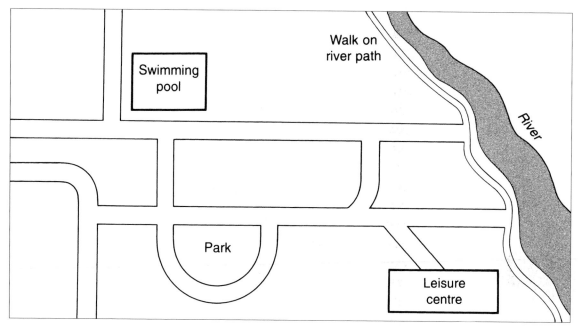

Figure 17   *A sample map showing leisure facilities*

ENVIRONMENT

As we mentioned briefly at the start of this chapter, our environment is the name for all the things around us. This includes where we live, the air, the plants, trees and flowers or the factories and the rubbish dumps around us, as well as the other buildings or fields, roads and railways.

The environment is which some people live in this country is mainly concrete and roads, high rise blocks of flats and factories. Others live in small villages with lots of green plants and trees around them, and see cows and sheep every day.

Some people live of the edge of towns, where there are lots and lots of other houses, each with its own garden, and not too far from the countryside. Caravans and houseboats are also places where people live, and this gives them a very different environment to most of us.

It is possible for many of us to change our environment, even if only on a day out. But babies and young children, and the very elderly or disabled need help to be able to do that. They have to have someone to take them out. This is one of the jobs that you may be doing as a carer.

There is some more information on environment, and some questions for you to answer in Chapter 3 (page 51).

RECREATION

This is what people do when they want to enjoy themselves; it may be at home, such as watching TV, painting or doing jigsaw puzzles. It may also be going out to enjoy themselves, or do something different. The recreation may be using green spaces such as parks, gardens, woods and forests. This may be walking or lying down, birdwatching, walking the dog and so on. It may also be going to the local Leisure Centre. Do you have a swimming pool you can use, or an ice skating or roller skating rink?

- Are there any recreational activities that you do, either in the college or away from it?
- Do you go to nightclubs and the disco for your recreation?
- Make a list of the leisure facilities in your area, and write a note about what you think of the ones that you use yourself.

Student exercise

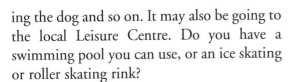 What do you think the following people should do for exercise and recreation?

- Shane and Vicky, who are in their early twenties, and are just married.
- Mrs Sturton, who is a retired widow living alone.
- John and Sandra, and their children who are 6 years and 8 years old.
- Mr and Mrs Curley, whose three children have now all left home.

There are some recreational activities which are much more risky than others; climbing mountains or boxing can be much more dangerous than walking the dog or dancing.

Student exercise

As a brainstorming exercise for all the class, make a list of recreational activities. When you have finished, see if you can work out what the risks might be with each activity.

RECREATIONAL DRUGS

This is one of the names given to the drugs which people take without having permission

from a doctor. They are usually used because people believe that they will enjoy themselves more if they take them. They include Cannabis (or Hash), Speed, E's, and other drugs up to the so-called 'hard' heroin and cocaine.

There are a lot of places where you can get information about these drugs. Find out what you can from local places.

Student exercise

1 In groups of two or three, pick one of the drugs to find out about. Get all the information you can, and then find out about all the risks of taking that drug. Then prepare a talk to give to the other people in your class to tell them what you have found out.
2 You can include a poster and some overhead transparencies, and this will help you with your key skills.
3 Keep your own work, and get copies of other peoples to put into your portfolio. Don't forget to say on it which is your work, and which is somebody else's.

SEXUAL BEHAVIOUR

This is something that usually starts around puberty, when you become a teenager. Some people consider it to be a recreational activity. Having sexual intercourse is something that is best left until you are older. It is actually illegal before the age of 16 years.

Like a lot of other activities, there are many risks that go with it. Unwanted pregnancies are one risk, but there are also many sexually transmitted diseases that can be passed on from person to person. A good way to help prevent both pregnancy and getting a disease is by using condoms.

Student activity

- Find out the names of as many sexually transmitted diseases as you can, and how you know when you have got it.
- You could do the same thing as with drugs, and work in small groups to prepare a talk for the others in the class.

SOCIAL CLASS

Social class is a way of putting people into groups depending on how much money they have and what their job is. You have probably heard people talking about 'upper class', 'middle class' and 'working class'. Upper class people don't always work, but they do own property or have a high income. Middle class people are almost always in that class because of their job. Working class people are in that category because they do the jobs that don't need many or any qualifications. The Registrar General of the United Kingdom has a system that divides everybody up into five different groups, and this list is still used today:

- **Social Class 1** – people who have high incomes, or own lots of property such as factories or office blocks. It also includes professional occupations such as doctors, barristers, engineers and other similar jobs.
- **Social Class 2** – Intermediate or Managerial and Technical occupations, e.g. police, nurses, teachers, pilots, farmers.
- **Social Class 3 (Skilled non-manual** occupations) e.g. Estate Agents, secretaries, clerical workers.
- **Social Class 3 (Skilled manual** occupations) e.g. drivers, joiners, hairdressers, butchers.
- **Social Class 4** (partly skilled occupations) – e.g. bar staff, agricultural workers, porters.
- **Social Class 5** (Unskilled occupations) – e.g. cleaners, window cleaners, road sweepers and bin men.

EMPLOYMENT

We know about some of the social factors that can affect out lives now. There are other factors that affect us, too.

Economic factors are one of them, and whether we have a job or not has a major influence on this. Economic factors involve how much money you and your family gets and how much is spent. 'Income' is the word used to describe the money we get coming in. It may be from wages, or it may be from benefits such as Jobseekers Allowance. Some people have an income that is not from either of these. They may own property, such as houses, flats, shops or offices, and get an income from letting them to other people. Sometimes, people have a lot of money from investing in shares, or winning on the pools or the lottery. This money is made to work for them (invested), and gives them a regular income.

Student exercise

Collect copies of your local paper, and some caring magazines such as *Nursing Standard* and *Community Care*. Look at all the different job advertisements, and see how much people doing different caring jobs can earn.

What difference will it make if the person doing that job lives alone, or has to support a partner and family with the same amount of money?

Wherever our money comes from, it will be very easy to spend it. Some will go on *financial commitments*, which are the things you cannot really avoid paying for. This includes (for most of us) somewhere to live, so we have to pay rent or a mortgage. There will also be the regular bills to pay, such as electricity, gas, water, TV licence, and tax bills.

Being employed goes a long way to help us in being able to pay these bills and to do the things we want. It also gives us a purpose in life, and becomes an important part of our identity. The first part of conversations with strangers is often about 'what we do for a living'. You can then say, 'I am a nurse', 'I am a labourer', or 'I am a shop assistant', and people will then make assumptions and fit you into a social class.

Health Screening and prevention

Health screening is a way of checking people out to see if they have any diseases or disorders, or if they are at risk of developing any. Prevention is a way to stop things happening such as disorders or disabilities developing.

The checks can start very early in life, for example with scans of babies inside pregnant mothers. This can show whether everything is fine, or whether all the fingers, toes and limbs are there. Advice is then given about what to do to stop babies being born handicapped in some way. Sometimes changing the mother's diet can help, or giving her some treatment such as medicines which will get to the baby and cure an illness. Sometimes the mother is told to stop smoking, or drinking, or taking drugs as the baby is being affected. There are some blood tests and tests of the fluid around the baby that can give an idea if everything is OK or not.

As a result of these tests, the mother may be given the chance to have an abortion as the baby is not developing normally.

When babies are born, they are checked by looking at them to see if everything is as it should be. Some disorders such as spina bifida and Down's syndrome can be seen quite easily at this stage. They also have their blood and urine tested. This can give an idea if all the organs inside are working properly. If they are not, sometimes they can be put right straight away but sometimes they may have to wait until the child is bigger. It may be that the child has to have medicine for all its life (if it is diabetic, for instance), or be on a special diet, for example for coeliac disease or PKU (phenylketonuria).

As we get older the Health Visitor will want to give us vaccinations to prevent us getting common illnesses which could leave us with disabilities if we catch them. These include measles, mumps, rubella, polio and TB (tuberculosis). Can you remember having any of these vaccinations? Some of them are by injection, but the polio one is often given to you on a piece of sugar.

The Health visitor or the doctor will also check out our hearing and sight.

When we get to school, other checks are carried out, and other vaccinations may be offered, or boosters to the ones we have before going to school, e.g. tetanus injections. Dental checks are given, and 'Nitty Nora' (a school nurse) comes and looks in our hair to see if we have any head lice that need clearing up.

When we leave school and go to work, we may have to have a 'medical' before we get offered a job. This is to make sure that we are fit and healthy, and should be able to do the job we want to.

When we go on holidays to far away places, we might have to have injections or tablets to stop us catching things like malaria or yellow fever.

X-rays and CAT scans are a kind of screening. They show up the things inside us so that doctors can tell if they are healthy or not.

Women are advised to have a regular 'smear'. This a cervical smear from inside the vagina, and is used to see if cancer is developing. If it is found early enough, this type of cancer can usually be cured quite easily.

Everybody is advised to have regular dental and eye check-ups, and hearing tests if you are worried about your ears.

At many chemist shops you can now get tests of blood pressure and cholesterol levels, which give an indication of how the heart and circulation are working.

Chemists can also let you have tests to check what is in the urine, e.g. sugar in diabetics, or for pregnancy. These are also a type of health screening.

PREVENTION

Types of prevention include all the advice given about not smoking, not drinking too much alcohol, and not taking drugs unless the doctor has given them to you. There is also a lot of advice about what to eat – the supermarkets have lots of leaflets about this. Things like eating less sugar and salt, and having five different kinds of fresh fruit and vegetables each day. Exercise is also recommended a few times a week. These subjects are covered in other places in your GNVQ, but they are all to help people to stay healthy and prevent illness.

Other ways used to prevent illnesses starting or spreading are to have clean water supplies and a way to get rid of the sewage. In the United Kingdom, water usually comes through pipes and taps, and the sewers are closed pipes so that the smells and bacteria are kept inside and away from people. The sewage is then treated to kill the bacteria (and the illnesses that they can cause).

Food poisoning is very common. That is why we should always wash our hands after going to the toilet, and keep them clean if we handle any food. People working with food (in cafes and so on) should wear gloves, and do a course in food hygiene. You may have done this yourself, either because you have a part time job, or from the college or school you are at. There is a person called an Environmental Health Officer (or HEO) whose job is to go round shops and cafes and other places where food is kept or handled and make sure that everything is being done properly and hygienically.

There are also rules about lifting and handling; these are especially important in health and social care where you may be having to move people around. The rules are intended for two things, one is to stop you injuring yourself, and the other to stop the person being moved from getting an injury. This topic is also covered in another unit of your GNVQ.

Another preventative measure which can stop you getting sexually transmitted diseases (as well as stopping a pregnancy) is to use a condom. Diseases are often passed on by the fluids which the body produces, and condoms stop the fluids from one person coming into contact with those of the other.

There are laws about infectious diseases which try and stop them spreading. Doctors have to report them to a central office (the

Community Health Physician) so that people that have been in contact with the disease can be traced and treated either to cure or prevent them getting the infection.

When they are in hospital, these patients will probably be 'barrier nursed' to keep them away from as many other people as possible.

Self-check questions

1 Can you name three types of health screening?
2 Can you name three types of health prevention?
3 Name two illnesses children are immunised against.
4 Who tests the hearing of children before they get to school?
5 What is the proper name for 'Nitty Nora'?
6 What does an Environmental Health Officer do?
7 The rules for lifting and handling are intended to prevent which two things?
8 Identify two things which condoms can prevent.
9 Why is it important to have clean water to drink?
10 Where do doctors have to report infectious diseases to?

Unsafe practices in the home or workplace

The things we will cover here link quite closely with things that are found in Chapter 4. You can use the work you do here as a start to that unit.

In the house

It is a well known fact that most accidents happen at home. This may be because we take more care at work or school and college than we do at home, or it may be that most people spend a lot more time at home than they do anywhere else. Accidents at home include such things as burns and scalds, falls, electrocution and poisoning. The two main groups at the highest risk are children and elderly people.

Many of the accidents could be prevented by thinking about things in advance, especially when children are living in the house. Inside the house, such things as fitting gates at the top AND the bottom of the stairs; putting kettles and pan handles out of reach, and sharp things such as knives and scissors are packed out of sight and out of reach. Make sure that windows are locked shut – or at least locked with no space for a child to climb through. Keeping doors to the outside closed so that they cannot get out without the parent knowing are also important.

Putting blocks into electrical plugs to stop little fingers poking inside is good idea, and to clear away any cables from vacuum cleaners, electric fans and so on as soon as possible to stop people falling over them. Other hazards should be tidied away as soon as you can, as well. Toys left lying arounds everywhere can cause accidents when people fall over them. Carpets, especially those put on to a shiny floor can cause people to slip and fall. Shiny floors are also a hazard when liquid is spilled on to them.

Make sure all the light bulbs are working, and that really bright ones are fitted where they are needed. Remember that older people may have failing eyesight.

Alcohol, especially spirits such as whisky and vodka, should be kept out of children's reach. If there is a cupboard with a lock to put them in, so much the better.

Figure 18   *Call a qualified person*

Medicines and cleaning things such as bleach and dishwasher tablets should be kept well out of reach of children – and always in the containers they came in so that the name of what it is can be read by anybody. This is important if old people are living in the house as well; if a bottle says 'Lemonade' or 'Water' but contains bleach, there could be a problem when somebody just opens it and drinks it without double checking.

It is all very well putting things on shelves and in cupboards out of reach of children, but how do you get them down again?

It is not a good idea to balance on chairs or coffee tables. Use a proper kitchen ladder or a very firm wooden chair to stand on.

In the garden

In the garden there should be a fence with no gaps for children to climb through, ponds should be kept covered with strong wire (or filled in altogether), and gates kept firmly shut. No poisonous plants should be allowed to grow there.

It is just as important to keep garden and garage things on high shelves with proper labels on as it is the things inside the house, e.g. weed killer and paint stripper. Once again make sure that sharp things are kept safe, and electrical cables do not lie about. A big risk is cutting though lawn mower cables whilst cutting the grass, or the hedge cutter cable when cutting the hedges.

Wearing strong shoes is a good idea if you are gardening, as they may stop the prongs of a fork or rake going through to your skin.

ADAPTATIONS

Where older people or people with disabilities live in a house or flat, there are changes which can be made to avoid accidents happening. Hand rails can be fitted in the places where they are needed; ramps put in place of steps so that people do not trip up; and stair lifts where people cannot manage to climb stairs. Kettles can be fitted to a stand which lets the water pour out without it having to be lifted up. There are many others, and some will be covered in optional unit 7. Boots the Chemists have a free catalogue which will give you an idea of the kinds of things available.

In the workplace

Health and social care workplaces are covered in detail in Chapter 4. The work here is more general, and applies to any workplace.

All workplaces in this country are covered by Health and Safety laws and by other laws which are different for different workplaces. If it is a place where food is handled or prepared, either warehouses, shops, cafes or supermarkets then food hygiene laws will apply. In places where dangerous chemicals are used, the laws and regulations called 'Control of Substances Hazardous to Health', or COSHH have to be followed. Where anything has to be moved and lifted, there are regulations covering that. The Manual Handling Operations Regulations (1992) applies to hospitals and residential homes as well as to factories and warehouses. People must be trained to lift and move properly to avoid hurting themselves.

All accidents in any workplace have or to be recorded. This includes any at school or college, as these are classed at workplaces.

Wherever protective clothing or other items are provided, they should be worn. They are there for a reason. This includes such things as hats, gloves, aprons, face masks, ear protectors, special shoes and glasses. There may also be time limits for how long you can do things, e.g. staying in a very noisy place, or a very hot one. Drivers must rest at least every five hours, and people using computers should have regular breaks from looking at the screen.

If you are taking any medicines which make you drowsy or sleepy, e.g. for hayfever, then you should not drive or be in charge of any machinery.

When you go to work or a work placement from school or college, one of the first things you should find out about are the safety requirements. Will you need any special clothing, or any training to do the job properly?

Student activity

Ask at library if there are any figures for accidents in the area that you live. You could also use the accident book of your school or college if the teacher/lecturer can arrange that for you.

Look at where most of the accidents happen, and what they were. If the figures are from the local area, see if the ages of the people are included, and look at which age group had most accidents.

Remember that this work links closely with Unit 4.

Indicators of good physical health

How can doctors and nurses find out if we are healthy or not? The first way is obviously

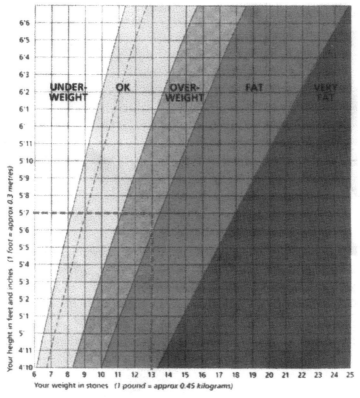

Figure 19   *A height/weight chart*

be looking at us, and also by asking us questions.

HEIGHT AND WEIGHT

They can also measure us and weigh us, and see if we are the right height and weight for our age and body type.

PEAK FLOW

This is a measure of how the lungs are working. This is done by using a 'Peak Flow Meter' which measures the speed that air flows out of the lungs when we breathe out. This tells us how well the lungs are working.

BODY MASS INDEX

This measurement also uses height and weight to work out how healthy people are. You have to work out a sum to get the answer, and then look it up on the chart to find out how healthy people are.

The sum is –

$$\frac{\text{weight in kilogram}}{\text{Height in metres squared}} = \text{Body Mass Index (or BMI)}$$

e.g. if your height is 1.82 metres, then divide your weight by 1.82 x 1.82.
if your weight is 70.5 kilograms, then your BMI will be

$$\frac{70.5}{1.82 \times 1.82} = 21.3$$

the answer will be slightly different for men and women.

Student activity

- Get the height and weight of everybody in your class, and work out their Body Mass Index.
- If you can use a Peak Flow Meter, you can also measure their lung function. Check if the people who smoke have the same results as those who do not.

Portfolio evidence

- To help you keep a record of information you will need for this unit, make yourself a UNIT DIARY to cover at least seven days. Seven pages from your A4 writing pad should be enough. Write the day you are starting, and the date, on the top of the first page, and the next day and date on the next page until you have enough for a week. (You can do this on a computer spreadsheet if you want, and it will be evidence of Key Skills.)
- You should keep a record of what you eat and drink, and what you have been doing; walking, dancing, sitting watching TV, playing football or whatever. Remember to include the time you went to bed and the time you got up, what exercise you have done, and what rest you have had. If you don't want to keep a diary for yourself, you can keep it for somebody else (for example your mum, dad, brother, sister, or friend).

- Start with breakfast on the first day and include any snacks you have between meals, and anything at all which you eat or drink until you go to bed. If you have a snack in bed, then that should go on the list as well. Also put in any exercise you have, for example 'Walked to school' or 'Walked to college', played football, had a bike ride, went swimming, went dancing, or whatever you did. Resting might be 'watch TV for an hour', or 'read the paper'. If you smoke, put down every time you have a cigarette as well. A new day starts at midnight.

When the weeks diary is finished:

- Look in the diary for the foods you have eaten.
- Was it a balanced diet? Draw four columns on a piece of paper, and have one column for each of the types of food (fat, fibre, protein and carbohydrate). List in the correct columns the foods you have in your diary.
- Work out how many kilojoules you took in each day. Your teacher will help you to do this.
- How much exercise have you had? What sort of exercise was it? Do you need to do any more?
- How much sleep have you had? Is it at least 8 hours each night?
  How much rest did you have?
- What were the risks involved in the things you have been doing?

Female BMI	Result	Male BMI	Result
Less than 18	underweight	Less than 18	underweight
18–20	lean	18 – 20	lean
21–22	average	21-23	average
23–28	plump	24 – 32	plump
29–36	Moderately obese	32 – 40	Moderately obese
37+	Severely obese	40+	Severely obese

MONDAY OCTOBER 11th

	Morning	Afternoon	Evening
Diet	Cornflakes and milk Cup of tea and toast Biscuits and coffee at break	Tuna sandwich Crisps Mars bar Can of Cola Chocolate biscuit and Cola at break	Egg, chips and peas with bread and butter Cup of hot chocolate
Exercise	Walked to school (1 mile) Used stairs instead of lift	Walked into town	Walked home Went swimming Danced in my bedroom for an hour
Rest		Sat in park for half an hour	Sat watching TV for 2 hours
Sleep			Slept for $8\frac{1}{2}$ hours

Figure 20   *Example hand-written page*

You can include here the results of the body measure tests you have done, such as your height/weight chart, the results of your Peak Flow test, and your Body Mass Index score. Index score.

- Which exercise was the most tiring?
- How did your body tell you this?
- Take your pulse before you do any exercise, and write down the number of beats per minute you counted.
- Do something energetic, such as dancing for five minutes, or riding a bike, and then take your pulse again.
- Is it different from the first time you took it?
- Why is this?
- Use the Peak Flow Meter if you have one, again for both before and after any activity.

Fat	Fibre	Protein	Carbohydrate
Burger	Cereal	Grilled chicken	Doughnut
Butter	Bread		Pasta
Milk	Vegetables	Cheese	
Chocolate			Fizzy drink

Figure 21   *An example list*

You could do this using two columns, one for **active,** and one for **non-active** pastimes, e.g.

ACTIVE   **NON-ACTIVE**
Swimming   Reading
Playing football   Watching TV

Now that you have all the information about what you have done for a week, make a plan for another week with all the improvements you think may make you into a fitter, healthier person. Say why you think the plan will make you into a fitter and healthier person. It will help if you use the headings from PIES to describe your plan:

PHYSICAL   INTELLECTUAL   EMOTIONAL   SOCIAL

ASSESSMENT EVIDENCE

You need to produce a health plan for improving or maintaining one person's health and well-being (*you may base the plan on yourself*). It must:

- use information from measures of health for the person
- include timescales and targets
- include a statement on how the plan might affect the person

To achieve a pass you must show you can:	To achieve a merit you must also show you can:	To achieve a distinction you must also show you can:
• understand the factors that affect the health and well-being of your chosen person by describing their state of health and well-being	• identify realistic short- and long-term targets for the physical health and well-being of the person	• produce your plan in a form appropriate to your chosen person
• list correctly factors which cause potential risks to the person's health and well-being	• correctly interpret two physical measures of health, and use them correctly in your plan	• justify the usefulness of your plan based on potential physical, social and emotional effects on the person's health
• use correctly at least one measure of health	• develop the plan using information from a variety of sources	
• provide basic ideas and targets for health maintenance or improvement within your plan		

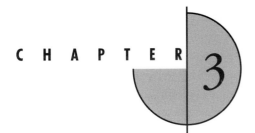

C H A P T E R **3**

Understanding personal development and relationships

. . . .

C O N T E N T S   A N D   L I N K S

When you are studying this unit, you will learn about:

- the stages of personal growth and development

- what social and economic factors are and how they can affect people
- how relationships can change over time and their effects on personal development.

L I F E   S T A G E S

After we are born, we do not grow up all at once. We start off as a baby, and grow over the next 80 years or so to become an elder. In between being a baby and an elder we go through five 'stages', which are called Life Stages.

These are:

- Infancy
- Childhood
- Adolescence
- Adulthood
- Old Age

Student excercise

  Before going any further, write down a sentence on each of the above life stages, saying what you think are the main characteristics of each one.

Infancy

This is the earliest stage, and lasts from birth until about three years of age. Our first stage of development as an independent person is when we are babies. We are unable to survive alone in the world, and need somebody there to look after us, and make sure that all our needs are met.

When babies are about a year old, they are often called 'toddlers'.

Babies always seem to need feeding and changing, don't they? The mother is usually the main carer, but not in every case. Premature babies (those that are born before they have been growing inside their mother for nine months) rely on nurses, doctors and machines to keep them alive.

Sometimes the mother is too ill to care for a child, or she has died. In these cases, some-

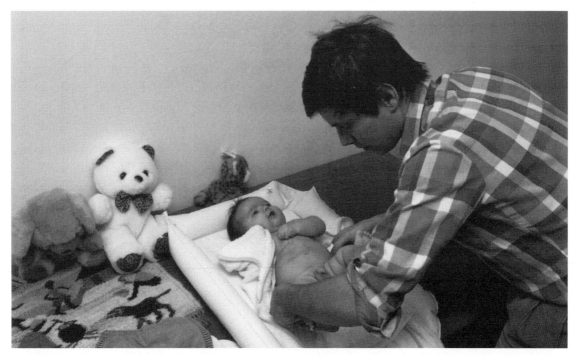

Figure 22   *A healthy baby*

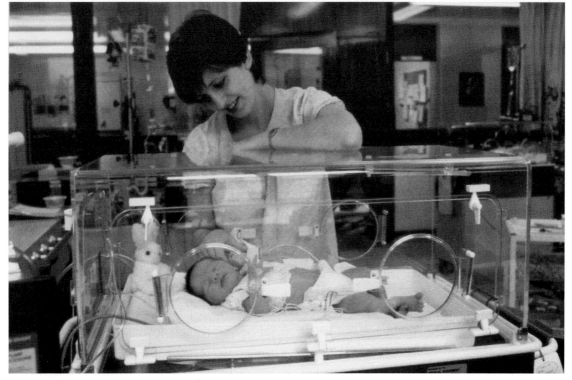

Figure 23   *Premature babies need extra care*

Figure 24   *Child with nanny*

body else has to take over looking after the baby. Sometimes mothers pay for other people to look after their children, such as a nanny or a nursery nurse.

Babies carry on growing and developing quickly after birth. *Growth* means to increase in size; *development* means increasing abilities, but they are very closely linked.

Baby won't be able to hold on to anything until the hands have developed enough to grip things, for instance.

There are certain 'milestones' a baby reaches as it is growing up. Each child does not reach these at the same time, but almost always they are reached in the same order, such as being able to walk, or to talk. There is an average age when things are expected to happen. This causes problems with some parents have the list and are very worried when

baby cannot do the things on the list on the day it is supposed to.

Self-check Questions

 Using the developmental chart on pages 42–43 write down your answers to these questions:

At what age may a child:

1   recognise mother?
2   Use 200 or more words?
3   Put their own shoes on?
4   Sleep for 20 hours a day?
5   Enjoy looking at picture books?
6   Not wet the bed for a whole night?
7   Say a few words?
8   Start to have temper tantrums?
9   Put everything in its' mouth?
10 Be able to build a tower from wooden blocks?

Childhood

Following infancy we come to childhood, which lasts from about three years to 9 or 10 years. The two main parts of childhood are the pre-school years (up to 4 or 5 years old), and the primary school years. The pre-school child is aged 1 to 5 years; the primary school years start at 4 or 5, and finish at 11.

P.I.E.S.

When people develop, it is in more than one way. Some of the ways we develop are:

Physically – when our bodies grow and change.
Intellectually – when our minds develop.
Emotionally – where we learn more about our feelings.

Socially – where we learn how to live with other people.

The initials of these words spell out P-I-E-S, which makes it easier to remember them. Think of apple pies or mince pies.

Student activity

- Why not organise a photo quiz for everybody in the class, and include your teachers?
- Get as many people as you can to bring in a photograph of themselves when they were a child, making sure they put their names on the back.
- One person has to do the job of looking after the photo's and a list of who they are. Put the pictures on to a large piece of card, or on to a notice board.

Figure 25   *From the age of three upwards, children begin to form relationships or friendships with other children*

Age	Physical development	Intellectual development
One month	Eyes follow moving objects, especially bright ones Able to hold head erect for a few seconds at a time	Likes gentle noises
Three months	Kicks strongly Eyes follow people around	Recognises faces seen regularly Responds to people by smiling or with excited movements
Six months	Can lift head and upper body with help (e.g. by parent holding wrists) Turns toward noises	Pays attention to noises Explores everything that can be touched Babbles
Nine months	Can stand up with support Will look at self in mirror May sit up May try to drink from a cup	Tries to talk, and may say 'mama' or 'dada' Shouts to get attention Knows the meaning of 'no'
One year	Can stand up using furniture as a support May start to walk a few steps Can grip with finger and thumb Can point to things	Responds to name, and follows simple instructions Can say a few words
Eighteen months	Can walk, including up stairs, and is starting to run Likes to push and pull big toys	Uses about 20 words, and can repeat many more Enjoys looking at picture books Can build a small tower of wooden blocks Can hold crayons and make scribbles with them, and shows whether s/he will be left or right handed
Two years	Runs about; climbs on furniture Throws things Can ride a tricycle	Uses more than 50 words, and can use them in simple sentences Asks what things are called Uses own name
Two and a half years	Controls all body movements Runs, climbs, jumps off low objects, and can kick a ball about	Uses 200–300 words Likes to listen to stories, especially with pictures
Three years	Walks upstairs putting one foot on each step May sit with feet crossed at the ankles	Can hold simple conversations, but is always asking questions Knows name, age, and whether they are a boy or a girl Is learning to count, and knows some colours Can copy simple shapes such as a circle or a cross

Table 3.1   *Developmental milestones*

Emotional development	Social development
Cries when hungry, thirsty, or in pain	Sleeps up to 20 hours a day Cries, but stops when given attention such as being spoken to or picked up
Likes a lot of attention, cuddling, tickling and so on Cries when this stops	Responds to carer's presence Gets excited when going to have a bath or a feed
May show anger May show fear of strange faces	Plays with fingers and toes Tries to get hold of feeding bottle Puts everything in mouth
Recognises individuals seen regularly, e.g. mother, father, brothers or sisters Likes a routine to be kept (for feeding, sleeping, playing, etc.)	Tries to imitate hand actions such as clapping
Returns kisses and cuddles Less afraid of strange faces	Can drink from a cup without help Can hold a spoon or fork Finds hidden toys
No major changes from one year	Can use a spoon to get food to mouth (messily) Takes off shoes and socks Has learned some bowel control Hands objects back to carer
Likes a lot of attention from mother or carer Has temper tantrums if not getting own way Plays beside other children but not with them	Will ask for food and drinks Can put own shoes on (but not tie any laces) Can feed self with a spoon and make only a little mess
Always active and into everything Emotionally very dependent on adults Does not like to share anything	Can use a spoon and fork to eat with Goes to the toilet instead of wetting nappies in the daytime
Beginning to share things Shows affection toward younger children Less likely to have temper tantrums	Doesn't wet the bed overnight

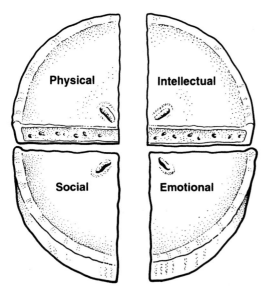

Figure 26   *Think of an apple pie*

- Give each picture a letter or a number, and keep a list of who they are where nobody else can see it:
  A – John
  B – Karen
  C – Sushita
  D – Mrs Jones,
  and so on (see Figure 27 on page 45). Don't let anybody cheat by looking at the backs of the photo's; they should write down who they think each photo is of, and at what stage of development they think they were (infant, child, adolescent, etc.)

Adolescence

Q u e s t i o n s

- As the primary years end at 11, does that mean that adolescence starts when you are 11 and go to the secondary school?
- What do you think?
- Were you an adolescent at 11?
- What does puberty have to do with adolescence?

Puberty is when the body of a child starts to change into the body of an adult. Things are changing on the inside where we cannot see and on the outside where we can see. Girls and boys end up looking very different from what they were and from each other between the beginning of puberty and the end.

ADULTHOOD

Starts as far as the law is concerned when we are 18 years old. That is the age when we can vote, and are considered an adult for most things. Adulthood can be split into different stages as well, as it lasts for such a big proportion of our lives.

Young Adults

As time passes by, we stop being an adolescent. Adolescents are often also called teenagers, so does that mean that on our 18th birthday we are grown up?

It does not really. We said before that the ages when we change from one stage of development to another are not exactly the same for everybody. But it is some time around our late teens or early 20s that we move on to become a young adult. We are often said to be young adults until we are about 40, or even 45.

Middle age

From 40 or 45, we become middle aged. This lasts until we are around 65 (some people say 60, because some women can still retire at 60).

Old age

After 65 we become old aged, or elders. This stage of life is getting longer as people stay more healthy and active. Some experts now

Figure 27   *Organise a photo quiz*

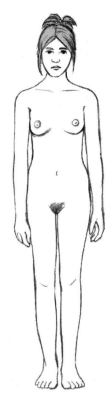
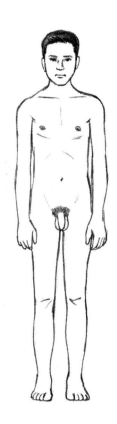

Figure 28   *Male and female adolescents*

divide older people into 'active elders' from 65 to 70 or 75, and 'elders' from then on.

It is still true that there are more older females than there are older males. This is because women tend to live longer than men.

Student exercise

Development exercise

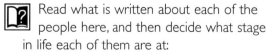 Read what is written about each of the people here, and then decide what stage in life each of them are at:

1 John takes the dog for a walk each morning before breakfast. When he gets back home he has something to eat and then sits and reads his paper and listens to the radio until lunchtime. After having some food, he goes to sleep in his favourite chair. Then he takes the dog for another walk, comes home for his dinner, and watches TV until about 9.30 or 10 o'clock, when he goes to bed. Once a week he goes to the Post Office to collect his pension.

2 Julie gets up in time to get the children ready for school and get their breakfast and packed lunch ready. After taking the children to school, she does the washing up and the cleaning and the laundry. Sometimes she goes to the shops on the way back from the school; sometimes she goes shopping in the afternoon when she goes to collect the children again.

3 Rafa wakes up every four or five hours and screams until he is fed. When he is not lying down, he is usually in his mothers' arms.

4 Kylie wakes up early in the morning and climbs over the side of her cot. She plays on the floor with her toys and anything else she

Figure 29   *Young adults and a child*

Figure 30   *An adult aged around 50*

can find, gurgling and talking to herself. She moves around in any way she can, gets into all the cupboards and any bags or boxes she can find around. The place is always a mess when Kylie is awake.

5   Florrie has help to get up in the mornings. She spends most of her day sitting in a chair reading. She likes the large print books she can get from the visiting library. She does not eat much, just snack meals a few times a day. In the evening she has help to get to bed, and watches television for about an hour before she falls asleep.

6   Wayne gets up in the afternoon, watches TV then goes out and gets something to eat at McDonalds. He goes round the pubs and clubs with his mates, and gets home to bed at around 3 o'clock in the morning.

Figure 31   *Contrasting images of old age*

Factors that affect growth and development

PHYSICAL FACTORS

Physical factors that affect growth and development start while babies are still inside their mothers. What the mother eats will make no difference to the baby, which takes all it wants first, so it is the mothers who will have the vitamin or mineral deficiencies, not the child.

Premature birth (when a baby is born before it has been growing inside the mother for 37 weeks) can affect a baby for all of its life. Some of them do not survive, most do these days, but may be smaller than other people of their age. They may also have heart and lung problems which need care for many years.

Drugs the mother takes are more risky; they will all get into the baby in the blood. If the mother is a drug addict, some babies are born addicted to the drug that the mother is addicted to.

Drugs are a factor that can affect development at any stage in life. Adolescence is the stage at which people are at the highest risk, and for some it goes on into adulthood and even old age.

Alcohol also passes to babies form their mothers blood, and if the mother drinks very heavily, the baby can suffer from alcohol poisoning. In really bad cases, the alcohol can cause body and brain deformities.

Alcohol, like drugs, is something that affects us all our lives. Adolescence is the start of alcohol use and abuse, and abuse can go on for as long as people are able to drink.

Smoking is another factor that affects unborn babies. Worse if the mother smokes, but also a factor when the mother is with other people who smoke, and she is breathing in the fumes.

Smoking once again is a habit that usually begins at about the time of adolescence. Some people stop as they become more mature, but there are still a lot of people who carry on smoking into adult life. Smoking related problems are the most common disorders that the NHS has to deal with.

Disease is another factor that can change a baby's life permanently, either something the mother catches before the baby is born (e.g. rubella, AIDS), or something they catch early in their lives and leaves a permanent problem; e.g. measles can cause permanent deafness.

Student exercise

 See if you can find out another two children's diseases that can leave you with permanent problems.

GENETIC FACTORS

Genes are the things which parents pass to babies that give the babies instructions on whether to go blue eyes or brown eyes, what height to be, the colour of the hair and the skin, ad everything else needed to make a human.

Sometimes the instructions in the genes go wrong, or there is a part of the message missing. Babies will then be born with something wrong with them. If it is something very serious, like having no brain (anencephaly), then the mother may have a 'miscarriage'. This is when the mothers' body gets rid of the developing baby because it knows it will not live. Sometimes the baby stays in the mother for the full nine months, but is born dead. This is called a 'stillbirth'.

Other genetic disorders leave the baby with a handicap of some sort. Some of these disorders are very obvious, such as Down's Syndrome. Some disorders are hidden, and perhaps even the person who has the problem does not know about it until they have grown up.

Student exercise

 Find out all you can about:
- Down's Syndrome
- Sickle Cell Anaemia.

Put the information you have found into a leaflet for parents who may be having children with either of these disorders. Tell them what the cause might be, and how to look after the child.

DIET

There is a saying that 'You are what you eat'. This is another way of saying that what we have in our diet affects out bodies. People who eat too much get fat.

People who do not eat enough are very thin. If there are things missing from the food we eat, other things can go wrong with the body. As examples, not enough vitamin C causes a skin problem called Scurvy; not enough iron can cause anaemia, and not enough vitamin D can cause the bones to be soft. This disease is called Rickets, and people who have had this when they were young usually have bow legs.

If people have any of these things wrong and it shows, they may get called names – 'Fatty', 'Boney' or 'Scabby' if it is a skin problem. Sometimes they will stop going out of the house so that they do not get called names. Or they may lose their temper very quickly when they are called names.

People can also be allergic to food, and it can cause changes to both the body and the mind. The most common thing is a rash or swelling of the lips and mouth. Many people are allergic to nuts, and if they eat them they could die. Some people are allergic to chocolate, and eating or drinking it can make them have a very bad headache, called a migraine.

Other chemicals found in food can change the way people behave. Some children who cannot keep still and are very naughty will get better if they go on a diet which leaves out the food additives that make them behave like that.

SOCIAL FACTORS

As you will have noticed by now, not everybody is the same. Some differences are physical – some of us are fat, some are thin, some are short and some are tall. There are also other differences that are more to do with the way we live and the place we live (the environment). Other factors which can make us change are what happen to us during our lives. It may be the people we meet or the things that we did. For example, if you have a relative who is in the police, and you like them a lot, you may decide you want to join the police force yourself.

The family

A very big influence on the way you grow up is the FAMILY that you live with. If your parents are farmers, you grew up with animals, plants and trees around you all the time. So when it is time to look for a job, you may want to do the same as them. Or you may have had enough of that and want to move to live in a city. In either case, spending the first years of your life with them has had an influence on you.

Not all families are like the one that you live in. There are many different types of groups which are still called a family. The first one most people think of is where there is a

Figure 32   *The environment you grow up in influences your life*

mother and a father with their children. Lots of families today will only have one parent, though. These are called 'one-parent families', and that parent is usually (but not always) the mother. There are fathers who bring up children alone, as well.

Sometimes children live with their grandparents, or just their grandmother. Many people get married more than once, and when a new parent is made in this way, they are called step-parents. So you get stepmothers and stepfathers; if they have children of their own, they are stepchildren to the new parent. Both sets of children will then have stepbrothers and/or stepsisters.

Children cannot always live with family members of their family, and other families will take them in as foster children or adopted children.

Student exercise

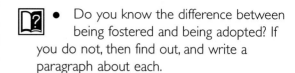

- Do you know the difference between being fostered and being adopted? If you do not, then find out, and write a paragraph about each.

The kind of family we live with during our childhood can have an influence on the way we behave and the way we are when we are adolescence and adults.

Student exercise

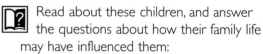

Read about these children, and answer the questions about how their family life may have influenced them:

- Chris is an only child aged 3. Both parents work in very good jobs, and Chris is looked after by a nanny in the daytimes. There are not many chances to meet other children.

Figure 33   *An urban family*

Because of this:

A Chris may not know how to share things with other children

B Chris may be very clever

C Chris may sleep a lot

- Joydip and Sanjay are aged 7 years and 9 years and live with their grandmother. Their parents work abroad, and can only come and visit a few times a year. Gran is quite old and cannot walk very far. She is also getting deaf.

Because of this:

A Joydip and Sanjay may not like each other

B Joydip and Sanjay may be very close to each other

C Joydip and Sanjay may speak very quietly

- Mr and Mrs Smith have both been married twice. They have seven children between them, and live in a ground floor flat with four bedrooms. The children are aged between 14 years and 2 years.

Because of this:

A The children may not get enough to eat

B The children may all be very shy

C The children may have no problem mixing with other people

- Lesley lived with her mother until her mother died of a drug overdose when Lesley was 9 years old. She then went to live with her gran, but gran got very ill and couldn't look after her any more. An aunt and her boyfriend took her in, but that didn't work out, and she had to go into care. At first she was in a childrens' home, but after a few weeks she went to some foster parents. That lasted a few months and then she went to some different foster parents. They wanted to adopt her, but she did not like them so she ran away. She had to go back to a childrens' home then.

Because of this:

A Lesley does not trust adults any more.

B Lesley wants to go to another foster home

C Lesley is a very happy girl

Education

Proper education starts when we go to school. In this country that is when we are 4 or 5 years old. The age is not the same for every-

Figure 34   *Teenagers in a children's home setting*

body. It depends where you live and when your birthday is. Some nursery schools start to teach children before they are 4 or 5, and if a child has special needs because they are disabled in some way, they can start their education as early as two years olds.

Going to a nursery or play group is often the first time away from home with people who are not members of the family. But for others, going to school is the first time away from a parent.

That is why you sometimes see little children crying and screaming and clinging on to their mother at the school gates. They are frightened to leave the parent in case they do not come back. They are not used to being left alone.

Children can go to private schools as well as state schools. If they go to a private school, somebody has to pay the bills. This is usually the parent or some other relative, but sometimes it is part of the parents' job. When a parent is in the army, for instance, they may have to go places where it is not safe for children. The army will pay for a school, then. Some of these schools are 'residential'; that means that you have to live there as well as go to lessons there. Parents also send children there because they think that they will be given a better education.

Some of the things that children do when they first go to school look like just playing. Things such as playing houses, playing cooking, playing doctors and nurses. These games help them to learn.

Children also like to do messy things, like painting or playing with water and sand.

Figure 35   *Children at play*

Student exercise

 ● How do you think that doing things like this can help children to learn?

When we get into the other classes, the lessons are more serious, and we have to listen to the teacher. When we get older still, we have to do more of the learning ourselves. That is what you are expected to do in this course. Do more of the learning for yourself.

Most people go to school until they are 16 year old. Quite a lot of teenagers do not like school, and stay away. This is called 'truancy'. Others behave so badly when they are there, that the school asks them to stay away. If they have to stay away for a short time, it is called 'suspension'. If they are never to be allowed back, this is known as 'exclusion', or being expelled.

Student exercise

 ● What effect do you think there will be on pupils who are suspended or expelled?

After 16, you can carry on being educated at colleges. After you are 18, you can go to colleges or Universities. You can also do educational courses at night school or by post. Really, when you think about it, there is no end to education if you don't want it to end. Even employers will train their staff to do the jobs that they need doing, perhaps in the factory, office or shop all the time, or perhaps with a day release course to a college.

Figure 36   *Messy play*

One reason people stop going to school, or want to carry on learning after they finish school is the influence of the teachers. Many people decide to be teachers themselves because they liked their own teacher so much!

There is no doubt, though that people with better and more qualifications tend to get the jobs before people without qualifications, and that they get paid better wages.

Self-check questions

1 At what age do children start school?
2 At what age can children with special needs start their education.
3 Why do some children cry and cling to their mothers at the school gate?
4 What is the difference between residential schools and ordinary day schools?
5 At what age can children leave school?
6 What is truancy?
7 What does being expelled from school mean?
8 What do you think of the teachers you have had so far in your life?
9 Which one or which ones have had the most influence on you?
10 Was it a good influence or a bad influence?

Gender

Everybody we know is either a man or a woman. It sounds so obvious and simple that we often forget what goes with those labels.

The shapes of our bodies are only one type of difference between girls and boys; gender differences are more about what people expect if people are male or female. Different clothes are worn, men and women take on differing roles in a marriage, jobs are not the same, and what we do in our leisure time may not be the same. There are also differences in personality and emotions shown; a common

one mentioned is that women are more caring, and men are more aggressive. There are many male nurses, though, and female wrestlers and boxers around.

When babies are born, the clothes bought for a male are not the same as those for a female (even if it is only colour), and get more varied as they get older. Toys for boys and girls are also different, and so is the way that people play with boys or with girls.

Student exercise

- Write down at least six ways that adults treat girl children differently than boy children
- Identify six toys or games that you think are more suitable for boys and six for girls
- Think of four jobs that are usually for women and four jobs usually done by men.

Our whole lives are affected by gender. Assumptions are made, and decisions about our abilities come from being either a man or woman. You must have heard the saying that 'big boys don't cry', and comments about 'women drivers'.

Ethnicity

This is the word used to describe groups of people who share certain features, such as country of origin, language, or racial features.

Environment

Our environment is the place where we live, the places we go to, and the things we use, such as the parks and the leisure centres.

One of the main parts of your environment which will affect your personal development is the place that you live in. The kind of places that most people live are houses and flats, and they both come in many different shapes and sizes. They are also different ages, and kept in different states of repair. A house with a leaking roof, or mould growing on the walls because of the damp is certainly going to affect the people living there. It is generally better for people to have space around them, so small terraced houses with two bedrooms are fine for 2 or 3 people to live in. If parents with 4 children lived there, it would be very crowded, and affect the childrens' development.

People also live in mobile homes, which actually stay in one place and are like big caravans. These are usually (but not always) out in the countryside, not in towns. Other 'mobile homes' really do move around a lot, such as gypsies and New Age travellers, who live in smaller caravans, converted buses, vans, and even cars.

Student exercise

- How do you think children living in a damp flat which is seven floors up in a big block of flats will be affected?

- What would be the effect on the seven children living in a two bedroomed terraced house?
- What sort of life would the children in a travelling family lead? How would their development be affected?
- If you had a free choice, what sort of home would you like to have?

Green spaces

Green spaces are an important part of our environment. Some of us have much more than others; those living in the countryside are surrounded by green space. Those living in towns might have a garden, but they may have to go and find a park or a playing field before they see any green spaces. There may be woods, commons, or forests near you. These are all good places to go for walks or picnics away from the concrete and bricks you see every day.

- Where are the green spaces that you can easily get to?

Figure 37   *New Age travellers*

- How often do you use them?
- What sort of other people are there when you go?

Student exercise

 What do you think would be the best sort of place for these people to live:

- Shane and Vicky, who are 21 and 22, and have just got married.
- Mrs Sturton, who is retired and widowed.
- John and Sandra, and their children who are 6 years and 8 years old.
- Mr and Mrs Curley, whose three children have now all left home. They live in the town, but want to move away.

Friendships

Getting out and about gives you a chance to meet other people. If you go to play tennis, you will meet other people who like to play tennis. If you play football, you meet other players. It is the same if you go dancing; you meet other dancers. These other people who are interested in the same thing as you can be called your 'peer group', and from these groups you will often make friends. When you are in college, the other people on this Foundation course with you are your peer group, and some of them will be your friends.

Do you hang around with a gang of people about your own age? They might live near you, but some may live further away. Friendships are another way we are influenced in our development.

If we want to stay friends with other people, we will often change the way we behave so that it fits in. This may be staying out later than our parents want us to, or smoking, or taking drugs, because all the others in the gang do. Or it may be going to the Youth Club on Thursday nights so that you can meet the others and do things like playing games or sport together. The influence of friends can be good or bad, and may mean staying away from school, or all going to get a Duke of Edinburgh's Award for Community Service.

We will be members of peer groups at all stages in our lives; people we work with, go to the pub with, or live near. Members of these groups will become our friends.

Student exercise

 Make a list of all the peer groups you think you may be a member of.

ECONOMIC FACTORS

We know about some of the factors that can affect out lives now. There are others, and economic factors are one of them.

Economic factors involve how much money you and your family gets and how much is spent. Both of these things can have an effect on your personal development. One of these effects is mentioned above; if your parents have the money and want to send you away to school, then they can do. If parents would like to send you away to school, but do not have the money to pay for it, then you probably will not go. 'Income' is the word used to describe the money we get coming in. It may be from wages, or it may be from benefits such as Jobseekers Allowance. Some people have an income that is not from either of these. They may own property, such as houses, flats, shops or offices, and get an income from letting them to other people. Sometimes, people have a lot of money form investing in shares, or winning on the pools or lottery. This money is made to work for them (invested), and gives them a regular income.

For most of us, the only way to make sure that we can manage from day to day is to have a job and a regular wage coming in.

Student exercise

- Collect copies of your local paper, and some magazines such as *Nursing Standard*, *Nursery World* and *Community Care*. Look at all the different job advertisements, and see how much people doing different jobs can earn.
- What difference will it make if the person doing that job lives alone, or has to support a partner and family with the same amount of money?

Financial commitments

Wherever our money comes from, it will soon be spent. Some of it will go on *financial commitments*, which are the things you cannot really avoid paying for. This includes (for most of us) somewhere to live, so we have to pay rent or a mortgage. There will also be regular bills to pay, such as electricity, gas, water, TV licence, and Council Tax.

If we have children, we have a commitment to them. We have to keep them clothed and fed, as well as ourselves. If we run a car, that becomes a commitment – even if it is one we can get rid of, if we really want to.

Other commitments might be paying off loans we have had to buy things, or a student loan that we used to live on when we were at college.

Think about what commitments you have, and which your parents have. Which ones could you manage without, and which ones you could not manage without. There are other ways to spend money, which are not really commitments. How much do you spend going to a nightclub, or the cinema, bowling, skating, or going for a drink?

Student exercise

Case histories

Look at these case histories and say what financial commitments you think each of the three people have.

NB if your teacher wants to add some figures here, you could have some numeracy key skills for your portfolio.

Figure 38   *Drowning in bills*

- **Lewis** rents a bedsitter. He is a student. The TV comes with the room, but he is buying a music centre on Hire Purchase.
  There is no washing machine, so he has to go to a launderette as he lives a long way from his mum.
- **Janice** is a single person with two children, aged 3 and 7. She lives in a council house. There is a TV, and a second hand music centre. Her income is from state benefits, and she borrows from a moneylender to buy Christmas and Birthday presents for her children.
- **Adrian and Maureen** are living together in a house they are buying on a new estate. They both have good jobs, and have borrowed money from the bank to put everything they want into the house. All the furniture and electrical goods such as TV, video, remote control CD player, washing machine, spin-dryer and dishwasher were bought with a bank loan.

Effects of relationships on personal development

PERSONAL RELATIONSHIPS

- We all have relationships with other people in our lives. The first relationships are normally with other members of our family; father and any brothers and sisters. There are also possible links with the members of our extended family –such as grandparents, aunts, uncles and cousins.
- We make another set of relationships when we start to do things outside the home.

Questions

1 When we are very small, where is the first place we are likely to go away from our homes and families and have time to meet and make relationships with other people?
   A – Playgroup
   B – School
   C – Work
2 Where do we make most of our relationships when we are aged between 5 years and 16 years?

Figure 39   *'Lewis'*

Figure 40   *'Adrian and Maureen'*

Figure 41   *Our extended family*

A – Church
B – Family
C – School
3 When are people most likely to have a
   serious relationship which could end in
   marriage?
   A – 14 to 16 years old.
   B – 18 to 25 years old.
   C – 50 to 65 years old.
4 If you are said to 'Have a good relationship'
   with someone, it means:
   A – You are married to them.
   B – You get on very well with them.
   C – They are related to you.
5 The age when people are most likely to
   have friend of the same sex is:
   A – 5 to 10 years old.
   B – 15 to 20 years old.
   C – 30 to 40 years old.

The relationship people have at different
ages are of different kinds. The first relationship we have are **dependency** relationships.

This is because a child is dependent on the
parents for all its needs. When people
become adults, there are still some dependency relationships, where one person relies
on the other for meeting all their needs.

Sometimes it is when a person is ill or
disabled and needs caring for. So a nurse or
a carer are in a dependency relationship with
their patients and clients. They are also giving them some **protection**.

Student exercise

- Arrange to watch children playing at a
  playgroup or in a nursery or nursery
  class. Have a look at how much they play
  together, or if they play by themselves.
- What do you think? The children may be
  playing near each other, but when they are
  between about two and three years old,
  they are not really playing together. They
  may fight because they want the same toy,

but that is not really playing together; the only relationship between them is that they are near each other.

- After about the age of three, there is some evidence of relationships forming. They will play cooking, or house, and one will be daddy while the other is mummy. They are sharing the game.

This is the start of friendship. When we start to go out of our homes and meet other people, we can begin to choose who to have relationships with. When starting school, there is a class full of other children. Some may know each other because they live near each other, and went to the same playground or childminder. A lot will be new faces, and that gives some choice in who to be friends with. We will have relationships with the others, and with the teachers and other staff at the school, such as the dinner ladies and the caretaker, but that does not mean we will be friends. A relationship does not have to be a friendship.

The same sort of thing happens when you move from the primary school to the secondary school.

If you go to college, you will meet another set of new faces. You will have relationships and decide to make friend with.

When you are sharing the same experiences, you can give each other **mutual support**. This is one of the benefits of relationships. As we get older, and start to notice the **physical attractions** of other people; the shape of their bodies, whether they have a nice smile, or if their hair is attractive.

Figure 42   *Play in the Wendy House*

Figure 43   *A power relationship*

When we have noticed any of these physical attractions, we start to look for a chance to start a relationship with them. This is how many romances start, and develops into a **sexual relationship**.

Another kind of relationship is the **power relationship**. The teacher in a class full of children is the person of power.

The carer in the Elderly Persons' home is the one with the power. At home, parents are the ones with the power. If you remember what we said above about dependency relationships, you can see that power and dependency are very close to each other.

All of these have a duty of protection for the person in the more powerful position.

- When we go to work, the people in charge are in a power relationship with us. The people we are working with have another kind; this is called a working relationship. You may not be friends with any of the people at work, but you can still get on well together when you are doing the job. If you like each other enough, you will start to see each other away from work, and become friends. The relationship will then become more sharing and supporting, possibly even becoming sexual.

Questions

1 Who do most of us have our first relationship with?
   A – friends
   B – parents
   C – teachers
2 When do we make our second set of relationships?
   A – When we start to go outside our homes.

B – When we start to walk.

C – When we start school.

3 What sort of relationship is the one between parents and young children?

A – Sexual

B – Dependency

C – Sharing

4 Which is a dependency relationship?

A – boyfriend and girlfriend

B – school friends

C – Nurse and patient

5 What is one of the benefits of having friends?

A – Mutual support

B – Power

C – Dependency

6 What kind of relationship might a physical attraction lead to?

A – Power

B – Sexual

C – Working

7 Read this short piece about relationships with parents, and then explain it in your own words. You may also want to have a class discussion about it, but write down what you personally think it means before you do that.

When I was five, my parents knew everything. When I was fifteen, my parents knew nothing. When I was twenty-five, I was surprised by how much my parents had learned in the past ten years!

The effects of relationships

Relationships can have both good effects and bed effects; or no effects at all. Read through the following situations, and then say whether you think the effects of the relationship described has been good, bad, or had no effect. Give reasons for why you decide what.

- Diane is 14, and her parents have just started to allow her to go out on Friday and Saturday evenings. They take her and collect her, and sometimes her friends. In the disco, she meets some other girls who are older than her. They offer her cigarettes. She tells them she does not smoke, but they call her a baby and sneer at her for being soft. She really wants to be friends with them, so when she goes the next week, she starts to smoke cigarettes.

- Darren is 15. He has just moved to a new flat with his parents. He does not know anyone around, but does not want to stay in. He goes out and just messes about because he is bored. He throws rubbish at cats and dogs, scratches cars, and throws stones at windows in empty buildings.

- He is kicking a can at a dog one evening when John and Mark come out of a house nearby and tell him to stop it. He gets talking to them, and they offer to take him to the snooker club they are going to. Darren did not know there was a snooker club, and had never played. He had seen it on TV, though.

- That was a few months ago, and Darren is now a very good snooker player, and goes to the club whenever he can, and hangs about with people he has met there at other times.

- Dahlia is 25 and went on an outward bound weekend with her colleagues from work. There were other people at the same centre when she was there. They were all staying for a week. She met Mark there. They became friendly, and did as much together during the week as they could. They even snogged a couple of times. At the end of the week, they gave each other their addresses and phone numbers. That was a year ago, and they have not made any contact with each other since then.

- Steve is 13 and not doing very well at school. He started to miss a day every week. The head found out, and called him in for

Figure 44   *Teenage girls*

an interview. Steve told him that one of the teachers was always picking on him, and that was the day he did not come to school.

- Walter is a widower living by himself. He felt very lonely, so he started dance classes on two afternoons a week. This took him out of the house, and helped him to meet new people, especially ladies. He started talking to Ellen, who only lived a few doors away from him. They soon started calling on each other for a cup of tea and a chat on the days they did not go dancing.

Figure 45   *Pensioners at a dance*

ASSESSMENT EVIDENCE

You have to produce a case study of the personal development and relationships of one person. It must include:

- factors that affect growth and development (for different life stages)
- effects of relationships on personal development

To achieve a pass you must show you can:	To achieve a merit you must also show you can:	To achieve a distinction you must also show you can:
<ul><li>identify correctly typical basic features of each life stage</li><li>identify and describe at a basic level at least one physical, social and economic factor</li><li>identify and describe different relationships from the case study you have chosen</li></ul>	<ul><li>show a sound understanding of life stages, especially how social and economic circumstances can affect personal development</li><li>identify accurately the positive and negative effects of relationships in the case study</li></ul>	<ul><li>make realistic suggestions about how a different set of physical, social and economic factors would have affected the development of the person in the case study</li><li>use examples to predict the effect that different relationships would have had on the development and self concept of the person in the case study</li></ul>

CHAPTER 4

Investigating common hazards and emergencies

CONTENTS AND LINKS

This unit links in with optional unit 1 (Investigating health and social care), unit 2 (Understanding health and well being) and unit 5 (Planning diets). It will also help to prepare you for first aid qualifications. In an ideal world, everyone should have regular first aid training so that when emergencies occur people around the victims can give the right sort of help immediately. Accidents occur in all sorts of places, but it would be extremely poor practice and very embarrassing if a care worker did not or could not give the emergency help required in a care setting. Accidents arise because a hazard is there – a hazard is a danger, so you will learn how to identify hazards and try to reduce them as much as possible. After you have learned about common hazards and emergencies by achieving this unit, you will be a useful person to know!

You will learn how to work more safely and effectively in care settings by being able to recognise common hazards and find ways of reducing them so that less accidents are caused. You will also learn how to recognise different health emergencies and how to deal with them and the general rules for health and safety in care settings.

Hazards and risks

Here is an example to show the difference between a hazard and a risk.

In Roseydale Nursing Home, there is a walk-in cupboard with a faulty lock that has been like that for a number of years. The staff keep meaning to do something about it, but the cupboard is in a part of the building that is not used very much. Files belonging to the owner are kept in the cupboard and he makes two visits each year to the home and Matron gets the files and puts them on a table the day before the owner comes. She is well used to the lock and seems to be the only person who can make it work. No one else goes into the cupboard. Matron carries a mobile phone with her at all times for emergency use.

The cupboard lock is obviously a hazard as someone could be locked in there for a long

Figure 46   *Faulty locks should be indicated and not used until repaired*

time. The risk of this happening is very low as Matron who can make a call on her mobile phone to get help only opens it twice a year. Nevertheless, imagine what would happen if Matron was on holiday or sick leave and someone who did not know the fault with the cupboard had to get the files. The cupboard should be labelled as a hazard and fixed as soon as it is noticed. The cupboard should not be used again until it has been repaired.

In care settings, hazards and risks can be caused by environmental (in the surroundings) factors and by people who may take short cuts in their activities or are careless in their work.

- Hazards can arise from:
- unsafe equipment
- dangerous substances
- infections
- moving and handling equipment and people
- fire.

Unsafe equipment

In the same way that care workers use substances which may be hazardous, they are also in contact with equipment which might be badly chosen, poorly manufactured or not maintained properly. Equipment will include simple things like chairs and tables or complicated machines like those which take X-ray pictures and ECG traces of the heart's rhythm. You may be asked your opinion of the design of a piece of equipment because you are using it everyday. Do not be afraid to state why you think improvements are desirable.

Daily use should mean that you always check the equipment before use and report any faults which you find to a supervisor. If the fault is serious, take the equipment out of use, label it as faulty and await the result of your report. The item should then be investigated, modified, repaired or removed from use permanently. In large establishments, there will probably be special forms to complete for faulty equipment.

Most items for use will have instructions for the manufacturer clearly displayed for you to read. Money for buying replacement equipment is often in short supply, but this should not mean that anyone has to do their job with unsafe equipment.

A lot of accidents still occur in care establishments involving 'sharps' which are not used properly or are disposed of incorrectly. 'Sharps' are syringe (hypodermic) needles, scalpels (very sharp hospital knives), broken glass ampoules (small sealed drug containers) and similar cutting items. Many workers who support main carers like doctors and nurses have been injured by sharps because the people who used them did not dispose of them correctly. They usually pick them up in ordinary rubbish and of course they cut and injure the person who may be a porter, cleaner or support worker. As well as a painful and unpleasant injury, there is the risk of developing a serious disease such as hepatitis or HIV infection. Such conditions are life threatening and so accidents must be reported straight away, however slight the injury.

Substances

In 1988, a set of regulations commonly called COSHH came into being. COSHH stands for the 'control of substances hazardous to health' and there was a period of time given so that people could alter their procedures to comply with the regulations. Every day people caring for others come into contact with a large number of substances which could have harmful effects on a person either in the place on the body where contact has been (called local effects) or affecting one or more systems of the body (called systemic effects). These harmful substances are said to be toxic or poisonous and this can occur soon after contact

or some considerable time afterwards. It can therefore be quite difficult to link the effect of the substance with a complaint suffered by the worker.

The types of illness commonly caused by toxic substances include skin irritations, asthma, headaches, feeling sick, vomiting, tiredness and not being able to sleep. There are many more. As you can see they are the sorts of conditions we all suffer periodically and few think about associating them with substances we may have used one day at work or even everyday. Many of these substances are familiar everyday chemicals we use all the time like disinfectants, bleaches, detergents, sterilising agents, antibiotics and even mercury from broken thermometers.

Dangerous substances

It is now compulsory for hazardous substances to be so labelled and the hazards listed together with instructions for dealing with emergencies arising from contact, spillage etc.

In addition, if you are asked to use hazardous substances at work, placement, school or college, you should be trained in their use. Employers must carry our regular risk assess-

Figure 47   *Hazard labels on some common materials*

ments on the use of hazardous materials and try to find alternative non-hazardous substances.

Infectious diseases

Infectious diseases are diseases which spread from one person to another (or from an animal or insect). They are caused by very small creatures which can often only be seen through a special piece of equipment known as a microscope. For this reason, they are often called micro-organisms, microbes or, by usually unqualified people, germs. Microbes commonly met in care settings are either bacteria or viruses. Both are very simple forms of life, viruses being much smaller and simpler than bacteria. Most viruses are too small even to be seen by the types of microscopes found in schools and colleges.

Student activity

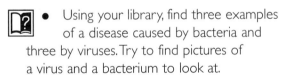

- Using your library, find three examples of a disease caused by bacteria and three by viruses. Try to find pictures of a virus and a bacterium to look at.

Viral diseases tend to have very short incubation periods, and short bouts of illness which come on quickly – there are several exceptions to this. Bacterial diseases are likely to have longer incubation periods and periods of illness starting more slowly and building up.

When people cannot see microbes they tend to forget their existence, so it is very important to protect yourself and your clients with cleanliness and good hygiene at all times. Everyone has microbes on their skin and in their bowels, these microbes are usually harmless and in fact give us some benefits. However, if these microbes get into other

parts of our bodies they can be extremely harmful. We call harmful microbes, pathogens.

Care workers in all settings are constantly dealing with clients who have been vomiting, coughing, sneezing, or soiling themselves, clothes, bedlinen, toilets and bedpans. Care workers are in constant contact with infected material.

It is important to understand that microbes can enter bodies in several different ways – by breathing in, from taking infected food, through any procedure where the skin is broken or cut (syringe needles, operations, injury etc) or special procedures where tubes may be pushed into the body e.g. catheters to allow urine to escape from a blocked bladder. Infection can even enter the body through sexual intercourse.

Care establishments are potential breeding grounds for microbes, they lurk in bed clothes, flower vases, sinks, toilets, bedpan washers, creams, ointments etc. Care clients are more prone to infection because of age, illness, lowered resistance from drugs etc.

Infections

A) FOOD SAFETY

This is a large topic and only an overview can be given for you here. If you decide to investigate food safety as part of your assessment evidence, you may need to get a specialist book on food hygiene from your library.

These are the main points in preventing infectious diseases from food:

- clean all equipment and surfaces after use with hot water and detergent, in some establishments anti-bacterial solutions may be provided – check the labels!

- wash your hands well with hot water and soap between all food preparation and cooking tasks
- never use the same utensils or surfaces for preparing raw or cooked food without thorough cleaning first. Raw foods contain bacteria, but these should have been removed during cooking
- thaw frozen meat and poultry thoroughly before cooking
- never use food after the sell by date and use food in date order
- serve food as soon as possible after cooking and keep hot, not warm
- dispose of all waste food immediately in the recommended manner of the establishment. At home, wrap in newspaper or plastic and place in a covered bin
- never allow pets where food is being prepared
- do not smoke when handling raw or cooked food
- have a high standard of personal hygiene and wash hands after visits to the toilet or touching any part of your body
- do not handle food if you are ill, particularly if you have nausea, vomiting or diarrhoea
- report any illness to your supervisor
- any cooked food not used within 24 hours must be thrown away
- make sure food is stored correctly and kept well away from chemicals such as cleaning materials
- make sure that pests, such as mice, rats and cockroaches are eliminated from kitchen areas
- cover food wherever possible and take precautions to prevent flies coming into contact with food
- make sure that refrigerators and freezers are working at recommended temperatures and not overloaded (should have thermometers fitted)
- keep door openings of cold storage facilities to a minimum and always make sure food has cooled down before placing in cold storage
- place cooked food at the top of a refrigerator and raw foods near the bottom; other foods should be placed in the special areas provided.

As you can see there are a lot of important things to remember with food safety and this is only some of them.

B) PEOPLE SAFETY

In most care settings, you will be dealing with bodily waste from clients such as urine, faeces, blood and other discharges, so it is extremely important to protect yourself and other clients. Some serious diseases are highly infectious and clients should be isolated wherever possible and strict personal and nursing standards applied. For instance, thorough washing of hands and the wearing of protective disposable clothing including disposable rubber gloves will help to limit the transfer of infection from one person to another. If non-disposable bedpans are used they must be washed in very hot water (at least 80°C), disposable equipment must be dealt with in the correct way. All spills must be cleaned immediately with disinfectant or special solutions. Clients usually share toilet and washing facilities and these can be a focus for carrying infection from one client to another. They should be cleaned between clients particularly if there is infection around.

Care must be taken when dealing with bed linen as millions of bacteria from an infected person can be thrown into the air, if linen is thrown around or shaken. Linen should be

Figure 48   *Handwashing is important in preventing infections*

changed daily and put into special bags. Soiled dressings and disposable items such as cotton wool, adhesive plasters must be incinerated (burned).

Always ask if you are unsure and try to think ahead. You do not want to be walking around with dirty dressings asking where you should put them. If you are dealing with any bodily fluids, you should wear disposable rubber or plastic gloves.

You will have noticed the frequency the 'washing of hands' has been mentioned, it is important, yet perhaps the simplest thing anyone of us can do to prevent infection.

Moving and handling people and equipment

This is an issue that is covered by the Health and Safety at Work Act 1974 (HASAW for short) and its subsequent amendments and the Manual Handling Operations Regulations (1992) and recent European Union regulations. The key point is that **training** in moving and handling people and equipment is compulsory if you are required to do this at work. This training is practical and can only be carried out by tutors who have attended special courses. Learning the basic principles in a textbook like this does **not** mean that you are trained to lift people or equipment.

Employers have a duty to:

- avoid manual handling operations so far as is reasonably practicable
- make risk assessments for any hazardous manual handling operation that cannot be avoided
- reduce the risk of injury as low as is reasonably practicable by prevention methods
- review risk assessments
- train and inform employees

Employers should either do away with the need to lift manually, change the way it is done or make adaptations to abide by these regulations.

Here are some general principles to bear in mind when lifting *anything*:

- wear clothing that will allow you to move easily and bend (many nurses and care assistants now wear trousers)
- wear sensible shoes that will not slip
- make sure that long hair, rings, jewellery or anything else cannot get trapped in equipment
- ask yourself whether you need to lift it at all
- use lifting equipment when it is available (after training of course)
- request the help of others when you need it
- make sure the area is clear of obstacles, is safe and appropriate e.g. the brakes on wheelchairs are locked, hand rails are down and so on.
- make sure that any person to be moved is clearly informed how and why the move is

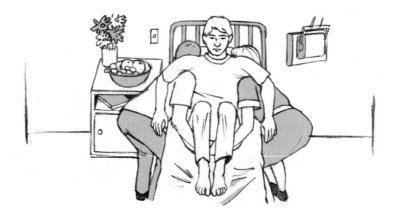

Figure 49   *Lifting a client*

occurring and understands their part in the process

- work with feet about hip distance apart, a straight back and bent knees
- know which grips and holds all of those taking part will use
- hold the load close to the body to minimise the stress
- if it is necessary, move your feet rather than your body
- **have regular training and assessment by experts**

Remember that the points listed above are for general guidance only and *you must not lift unless you are qualified to do so*. If you damage your back, not only will you suffer unnecessary pain and disability, it could be the end of your working life in care. If you are still a middle years teenager, you should not be lifting heavy loads at all.

Fire

In care settings there are many clients who are physically unable to help themselves because of infirmity, disability, illness, unconsciousness or surgery. In addition, there are people unable to follow instructions, confused and disoriented people and children too young to understand dangers. All these people are more exposed to danger of all types but, particularly fire because they cannot either remove themselves from the danger or take steps to deal with the situation. This is why you should be able to help prevent hazards by recognising unsafe conditions and unsafe equipment. Learning about fire safety is part of everyone's job. Each person must know how to prevent fires, sound alarms, or if appropriate remove clients and fight **small** fires. There are four main ways in which fires start in care settings.

In the past, careless handling of tobacco products, particularly cigarettes, caused most fires in care settings. Fortunately, most hospitals and care premises are now 'No Smoking' areas, but this may mean that people who ignore the rules put out cigarettes quickly on being spotted and may not do so properly. You must know the rules about smoking in establishments where you work or learn.

Main causes of fire in care settings

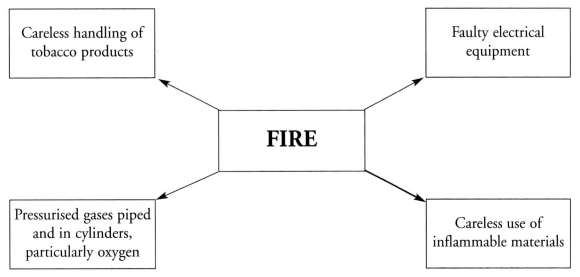

Electrical equipment may cause fire if it is not used correctly, faulty or old and in poor condition.

Piped or cylinder oxygen is required to help some people breathe more easily. It is under pressure and can cause explosions or make an existing fire much worse. Many other materials used in care settings may also, if not used correctly, cause explosions or catch fire. Such material is called inflammable or sometimes flammable and should be clearly labelled so that people using it are aware and constantly reminded. Many cleaning materials and substances used in routine maintenance are inflammable. Waste material is often a cause of fire if it is left lying around. Some years ago, a busy underground station in London caught fire causing death and injury to many people through smoke inhalation and a panicking crowd. The fire investigation, which followed, showed that a carelessly tossed cigarette had ignited rubbish left under the elevator. Since that time, there has been a massive clear up of rubbish in public places.

Many clients in poor health live in their own homes and hazards from cooking frequently cause fires. The most notorious of these is the unattended chip pan (the non-electrical type); people don't mean to leave the cooker unattended, but the telephone rings, someone calls or it can simply be forgotten about. The pan overheats and the oil catches fire. If you suspect a client may be unsafe cooking on his or her own, inform your supervisor in writing, date and sign the memo.

Ways of identifying and reducing risks in care settings

People have become far more aware of the need to protect people in workplaces in the last 20 to 30 years and the awareness has been reinforced by legislation (laws) such as HASAW and COSHH and the large sums paid out in compensation to the victims through the courts. Recently a small boy on a school trip to an open farm has been awarded

Figure 50   *Cooking hazards frequently cause fires in the home*

about several million pounds after being severely disabled through contracting salmonella infection.

Some of the ways in which hazards are identified and reduced are:

I ENVIRONMENTAL SURVEYS AND AUDITS

This means that an individual or a group of people is designated to go round an establishment with a checklist and look for general and particular hazards. Sometimes they will be checking only electrical equipment and obviously these people must be specialists in electrical systems. The Fire Service carries out checks of premises to advise on fire risks. The Health and Safety Executive inspectors may look at kitchen hygiene in a restaurant or look at safety systems in a steel mill for example. As there are only limited numbers of inspectors of this kind, legislation has placed health and safety clearly on the shoulders of employers and they are now required to carry

out annual health and safety checks themselves. Many employers also have health and safety representatives belonging to unions and they assist in bringing hazards to the notice of employers and making sure that the hazard is reduced. The COSHH regulations require employers to carry out regular risk assessments of hazardous substances. In most organisations, the employer does not actually do this himself, but has a designated Health and Safety Manager to organise this; however, the employer is still responsible in the eyes of the law.

2 STAFF TRAINING

You have already come across this several times in this chapter and have learned that training forms an essential part of any health and safety legislation. In the past, when emergencies occurred, investigations afterwards showed that far too many staff were ignorant of basic procedures and so this has now been covered by legislation. Health and safety is now everybody's business and the HASAW makes this very clear.

Some of the types of training staff in care settings must have includes:

- fire safety
- manual handling and lifting
- correct operation of any new equipment
- handling substances hazardous to health
- preventing cross infection (from person to person)
- security including dealing with violent clients and visitors

It is important that training occurs on a regular basis and is not a 'once only' exercise, so many types of training occur regularly, perhaps every one or two years.

3 REGULAR CHECKING AND SERVICING OF EQUIPMENT

You have also learned that maintenance is required regularly in care settings and here are a few examples:

- qualified electricians should carry out annual checks of appliances and equipment and be used to install and repair electrical equipment; never attempt to make a small repair yourself when you are in a work setting
- be on the lookout for frayed flexes, cracked or broken insulation, trailing wires and report these verbally and in writing to your supervisor
- oxygen cylinders should be stored in designated areas with caps on their valves
- only special electrical safe equipment should be used where oxygen may be required
- authorised persons should regularly test equipment used alongside oxygen to make sure that there are no leaks
- it is part of everyone's job to report any equipment that is faulty, even broken chairs and tables put labels on saying 'Faulty', take them out of use and report to a supervisor.

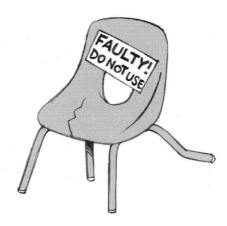

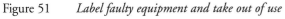

Figure 51   *Label faulty equipment and take out of use*

4 PUTTING IN PLACE RULES AND REGULATIONS RELATING TO HEALTH AND SAFETY

Rules and regulations relating to health and safety may be devised by as large a body as the European Union or the British government. Medium sized bodies such as Health authorities or National Health Trusts or much smaller establishments such as individual residential or nursing homes and child nurseries. They are all designed to protect clients and care workers, reduce accidents, prevent emergencies and save money in rebuilding and refurbishment. You should respect all rules and regulations as part of your role in society and good citizenship as well as being an employee or a student on work placement. Many of these rules have arisen as a result of investigations taking place after serious accidents that have resulted in death and injury of individuals. They are not there to stop people enjoying themselves, but there because authorised people have deemed it to be necessary.

One of the most important pieces of legislation that we all have to abide by in our employment is the Health and Safety at Work Act 1974 and all its later additions.

Some of the key principles stated by this act of parliament are:

HEALTH AND SAFETY REGULATIONS

The main law controlling health and safety is the Health and Safety at Work Act passed in 1974.

 The key points from this act are as follows.

- Employers must protect the health, safety and welfare of the people who work for them. The act states that this is 'as far as is reasonably practicable'.
- If a person continuously takes no notice of the systems the employer tries to put into place, then the employer cannot be blamed if anything happens to the employee. Also, of something happens totally 'out of the blue' and nobody could have expected that to happen, the employer is not at fault.
- Your employer has a duty to make sure that while at work you are reasonably safe. If you are injured at work while employed you may be able to take your employer to court for payment for your injuries.
- The list below states the main duties of an employer towards the welfare and thus the safety of their workforce by following procedures to

1 keep the floors clean
2 maintain floors and passageways
3 prevent overcrowding
4 keep the room temperature above 16°C
5 make sure there is good ventilation (fresh air) and lighting
6 provide suitable toilets and places to wash with soap, hot and cold water and something to dry hands with
7 provide drinking water and somewhere to eat meals
8 employ people who are trained and competent to do the job
9 provide the right equipment, protective clothing and materials for the job
10 check that you take reasonable care with equipment
11 guard all dangerous machinery
12 provide first aid kits and someone trained in first aid

13 provide fire fighting equipment and training for fire hazards.

However, it is not only the employer who has duties, everyone also has to

- take reasonable care of their own health and safety
- take reasonable care for the safety of your fellow workers
- co-operate with the employers in health and safety matters
- not interfere with equipment provided for health and safety.

Health and Safety Executive personnel have powers to take people to court, close places down or ask for them to be improved within a set time period. People who break health and safety laws can be sent to prison or fined.

Student activity

 - Choose one care setting and write a report on the employer's duties in that care setting, state how each key point is met. You may need to measure temperature and calculate space.

- Try to find the safety policy of a care establishment – this is a written statement of the safety rules and regulations and how they are carried out e.g. a local hospital may ring the fire alarm bells every week at the same time, to check that they are working properly. Hazards should be identified and procedures in place for monitoring, officers should be named and staff informed of dangers and precautions to be taken.

Many establishments also have a code of practice. The Government has been responsible for the introduction of various charters. These documents all state the standards of the organisation, what people can reasonably expect from the service, especially with responding time, and where they can complain. You should know these principles.

Student activity

- Collect three copies of different charters and write a report comparing the detail in each one. Do people know the charters exist? Do they read them? Have they ever used them? You could survey this!

Another government document of great importance is the Fire Precautions in the Workplace regulations 1997 that deal with the responsibilities for fire. It has many subsections but deals with fire fighting and detection, emergency routes and exits and maintenance. Responsibility is placed firmly on the shoulders of the employer to comply and on every employee to play his or her part in taking responsibility by training, fire detecting, being aware of and reporting hazards that may lead to fire. If you would like more details on these regulations because you are surveying fire precautions in your assessment audit visit website www.hmso.gov.uk/si/si 1997/97184001.htm, you will find pages 6 and 7 the most valuable. These points are also covered in section 6 on 'providing safety and warning notices'. You have already learned about COSHH regulations that deal with controlling hazardous substances and the importance of clear labelling, training and finding alternatives which are less hazardous.

5 PUTTING IN PLACE POLICIES RELATING TO PERSONAL AND GENERAL HYGIENE

There are two important areas for you to consider here. The first is HASAW that relates to everyone, their personal cleanliness and their protective clothing. It ensures that employers provide correct hand-washing facilities, toilet areas and rest rooms. The second deals with food hygiene and safety where it is even more important that these facilities are provided.

6 PROVIDING SAFETY AND WARNING NOTICES

You have learned about the importance of notices on faulty equipment, but there are other important safety notices. When you walk around public buildings during cleaning, you cannot have failed to notice warning notices such as 'Wet Floors, Caution', Emergency Exit, Fire doors and so on.

The Fire Precautions Act is very specific about notices, for example:

- all emergency and ordinary exits shall be kept clear at all times and lead to places of safety
- emergency exits and exits must be appropriate for both the size of the building and the largest number of people who might be within
- emergency doors must open outwards in the escape direction, and not be locked or fastened such that they cannot be easily opened in an emergency
- sliding, revolving doors and lifts should not be classed as emergency exits
- emergency routes must be clearly signed and if lighting is required should have emergency lights in case of a power failure

The next section states that emergency equipment must be kept in working order and good repair and a system of regular maintenance be in place.

In addition to the 'fire' notices, you will see other doors with notices forbidding entry

Figure 52   *Warning notices should be displayed prominently*

to rooms containing potential hazards; such notices can be seen particularly around hospitals in areas of X-rays and other radioactivity, microbiological laboratories, drug stores and so on.

Student exercises

1 In small groups of 3 or 4, select small areas in your school or college to try out a mini survey. Find all the hazards that you can and write them on post-its. In the whole class, take a large sheet of paper (a flip chart sheet would be good) and divide into 3 columns headed high risk, medium risk and low risk. Each person places a hazard post-it in the appropriate column and explains their reason for choosing that level of risk. The class members might discuss the finished sheet and make copies for their files.

2 After learning about a topic, each person prepares at least one question to ask an expert working in the field of health and safety. People who might be prepared to talk to you could be:
   ● Health and Safety manager
   ● Fire officers
   ● Catering manager
   ● Laboratory technician

3 Ask your tutor if you could take the Food Hygiene certificate, if doesn't take long to study (about 12–15 hours) and it would be very useful if you require casual work in a food establishment.

4 Design a questionnaire to give to your cleaners, laboratory technicians or porters to find out how working with cleaning materials or laboratory chemicals complies with COSHH, how lifting heavy loads complies with Manual Handling Operations regulations.

5 Ask permission to visit the canteen or refectory kitchens and have food safety points explained practically.

6 Ask your tutor to provide some copies of the Health and Safety at Work Act as they are displayed for employees. In groups of four or five, discuss what the act means to you in your learning establishment and make a list of the main points on a flip chart sheet. In the whole class, discuss the differences and similarities of the charts.

Self-check questions

1 Who is the person who carries the highest responsibility for health and safety in your school or college?
2 List four key points in making food areas safe?
3 Name three important acts or regulations that are important in health and safety.
4 List four key points relating to emergency fire exits
5 Who carries responsibility for health and safety under HASAW?

ASSESSMENT IDEAS

For your assessment evidence you are required individually to carry out a workplace health and safety audit or survey. In this audit, you will identify the hazards and state what might happen if the correct health and safety practice is not followed. For example, if you find a lot of rubbish in a stair well, someone might be secretly smoking in the stairwell and in hurriedly stubbing out the cigarette leave it smouldering in the rubbish. This might lead to fire and smoke inhalation. People's lungs might be badly damaged, or worse people might suffer burns. For each hazard, try to think of at least two effects. You might choose your learning centre, workplace or a care setting in which to do this survey.

Always ask permission first from the person in charge, explaining clearly what you are going to do. Of course, you will hope that you do not find many real hazards because the management of health and safety is good. In this case, make sure that you mention all the health and safety features you have noticed, such as warning notices, signs on exits, push down bars for easy emergency exits and so on.

You might choose to survey particular services rather than be general; you could survey wash rooms, toilet facilities, changing rooms and rest rooms for a week checking on availability of soap, hot water, hand drying equipment, working toilets, toilet paper and so on. Other areas you might choose could be

- First aid boxes and sick rooms
- Laboratories
- Kitchen areas
- Teaching rooms, common rooms and corridors
- Exits and emergency exits
- Fire fighting equipment

Check your choice with your tutor before you begin.

If you are aiming for a merit grade, you will need to be very accurate in your survey and give the location of the features you survey. You could make a plan of the building and draw symbols or colour code the different features. If you are better at writing, you might draw up a chart saying which room, what feature and its condition and do not forget to include the effects it might cause if it failed.

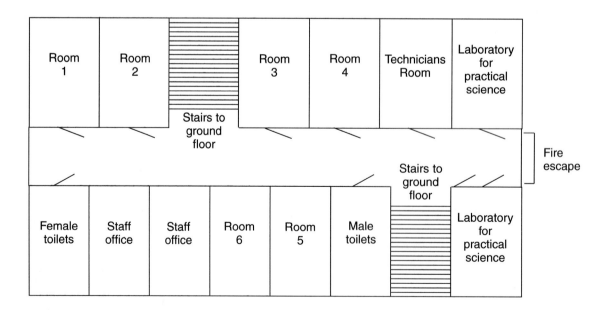

Figure 53   *Plan to show First Floor of North Block*

And so on…

If you are trying for distinction level, you will need to give the exact location of the health and safety features and say how they help to reduce risks and what the hazard would be, in addition to the work for merit.

You might say that the window blinds covered the windows that ran the whole length of the room facing the sun. They were kept in a good state and could be easily opened and closed. They kept the temperature of the room cooler in the summer and stopped people getting headaches from the glare of the sun. You will also need to make realistic suggestions for improvements resulting from your survey. For example, you might wish the cleaners to check a stairwell everyday to clear any rubbish, this might be realistic whereas saying that someone should be in the stairwell at all times to stop people smoking there is unrealistic. To finish this section, you might like a simple statistic!

2% of accidents are easily prevented

50% of accidents are practically preventable (in other words if we did something about it, we would reduce half the accidents)

98% of accidents are of the preventative type, in other words only 2% of accidents are unavoidable – that is something to think about!

Chart to show the results of a survey of health and safety in North block teaching area 16th May 2000			
Location of room or corridor	Hazards noted	Effects of hazard	Health and safety features
Room 1	broken chair	person could be injured	all other furniture in good repair
	light switch loose	electric shock	other switches and sockets, electrical equipment O.K.
	cupboard door won't close	person could be injured	window blinds to shut out glare of sun
			fire exit sign on door saying where to go
Room 2			

Figure 53

Dealing with emergencies

You should be able to deal with common personal health emergencies that might occur in care settings; however, bear in mind this knowledge is very valuable in any place at any time!

Asthma, fits, concussion, burns and scalds, recovery position

ASTHMA

This is a condition which causes difficulty in breathing, particularly in breathing out. Many adults have asthma, but it occurs more often in children and young people. It can occur in any care setting.

Key signs

- Difficulty in breathing – often wheezing.
- The sufferer will often be anxious or upset.
- There may be blueness of the lips and skin generally.
- If a severe attack is present, the asthma does not respond to treatment or occurs for a long time – then call the ambulance or doctor.

What to do

1 Keep calm and reassure the person.
2 Sit the person forward at a table or similar surface with plenty of fresh air.
3 Help the person to take medication if this is with them.
4 Watch for signs that it is not getting better.

Most asthma attacks are triggered off by worry or the presence of some substance to which the person is sensitive (allergic). Many people are sensitive to animal hair, dust or pollen. However, asthma sufferers tend to have more attacks if the atmosphere is smoky or they have a respiratory infection. People who often have asthma attacks usually carry inhalers, this is like an aerosol (spray) which puffs out a certain amount of a special drug into their mouths and down into their lungs to help them breathe more easily.

You should monitor a person who is having an asthma attack by taking the pulse and breathing rate about every 10 minutes.

Taking the pulse

This represents the heart beat and can be felt where an artery is close to the surface of the body. The most common place to feel for an artery is at the wrist, below the base of the thumb. In babies, the wrists are very tiny so it is easier to take the pulse of a larger blood vessel on the inside of the upper arm. However, in an emergency or life threatening situation, these pulses may be hard to find because the blood is being pumped around the body slower and the pulse is becoming weaker, so the pulse at the neck is more useful. This is found between the windpipe of the neck and the muscle which runs from the ear to the lower part of the neck in the middle. All these pulses can be found on both sides of the body.

To find someone's breathing or respiratory rate, watch the rise and fall of a person's chest and count. The rib cage will move up and out and return to its first position. This is one breath. It can be difficult when a person is clothed, you can also watch for the 'tummy' moving in and out or the sounds of breathing. Breathing rate is much slower than pulse rate but it too increases with infections, fever and exercise.

EPILEPTIC FIT

There are a few types of fit. In babies and young children, a fit is common when the body temperature is raised well above normal. This is known as a fever and the type of fit is often called a febrile (which means feverish) convulsion. You may come across this in any care setting involving babies and young children.

Key signs

- Hot, pink skin and sometimes sweating.
- Muscle twitchings, arched back, clenched fists.
- Breath holding, redness or even blueness of face.
- Drooling at the mouth.

What to do

1 Make sure the child cannot injure itself – you can put padding or pillows around.
2 Remove clothes and bedclothes to cool the child.
3 Sponge with very slightly warm (tepid) water, starting at the head and working down.
4 If necessary, place the child in the recovery position to keep the airway open.
5 Reassure others who may be frightened that the fit is rarely dangerous, but the high temperature has to be looked at by qualified medical help. Often this will mean calling an ambulance, but if at home, the child's own doctor may be called more quickly.

Major fits or grand mal fits will often occur quickly, sometimes with a warning sign, such as odd behaviour, strange smell or taste and sometimes without warning at all. Anyone can have a fit, but people who have brain damage or head injuries are more likely to have regular fits. This means clients in residential establishments, nurseries and hospitals are more likely to have fits.

Key signs

- The individual suddenly becomes unconscious and falls.
- The back is arched and the muscles stiff.
- Breathing usually stops and this causes a blueness around the face and neck.
- Muscles start to contract and twitch, breathing becomes noisy.
- The individual may pass urine or open their bowels during the fit.
- The muscles relax and breathing starts again within a few minutes.
- The person recovers consciousness and may sleep for a while or appear dazed.

What to do

1 Make sure the client has space around and try to protect from injury by easing the fall or pillowing the head.
2 leave the client unrestrained, leave the mouth alone and let the client remain where they are unless in a very dangerous place.
3 Loosen clothing around the neck.

4 Stay with the person and place in the recovery position when breathing starts again.

5 If the fit lasts for more than a few minutes call an ambulance.

6 If the fit is the first or it is followed by more fits, call the ambulance or doctor.

CONCUSSION

This is when the brain inside the skull has been shaken by a blow of some sort to the head. If you have ever made a jelly or a blancmange in a mould and shaken it to release it, it often has tiny tears in the outside. This is similar to what can happen to the brain after a blow. A blow to the head can happen in any place and therefore in any care setting. Older people and adventurous children often fall and are particularly likely to become concussed.

Key signs

- Brief loss of consciousness.

- Mild headache.
- Feeling of dizziness or feeling sick on recovery.
- Loss of memory of what happened.

What to do

1 Watch closely for any worsening of condition after recovery.

2 Do not allow the person to just carry on. The person should always see a doctor, this usually means being taken to hospital. In some cases you might have to call an ambulance, but the person could be taken by car.

3 However, if the person does not become conscious quickly, say after three minutes, place in the recovery position and call an ambulance.

In several care procedures now, you have been told to put the individual in the recovery position.

As well as concussion, a person may have suffered a head wound that is bleeding. There may also be other cuts that will need treating.

RECOVERY POSITION

This is the position for an unconscious or dazed person who is breathing and has a pulse.

Kneel beside the person who should be lying on the back with legs straight. Tilt the head back and lift the chin to allow air to get to the lungs. Place the arm nearest to you out and bend up at the elbow, with the palm of the hand facing you.

Now, bring the other arm across the person's chest, holding the hand against their cheek with the palm outwards again. Notice both palms face outwards. With your other hand, pull up the knee of the far leg keeping their foot on the ground.

With your two hands in this position, carefully and gently pull the person towards you until they are resting on their hand underneath the head and the upper leg, the one you pulled is supporting the body bent at the knee (see Figure 54).

Adjust the position of the head so that it is still tilted back and make sure the person is in a secure position. Monitor pulse and breathing regularly, keeping records if you can.

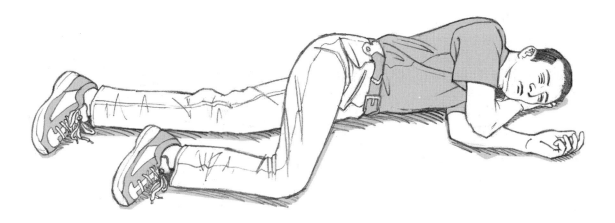

Figure 54   *The final stage of the Recovery position*

BURNS AND SCALDS

A burn is caused when dry heat damages the body, like touching a hot pan on the cooker and a scald is an injury from wet heat, like steam from a kettle.

These injuries can occur in any setting, but are more common with toddlers and young children, who often do not realise the dangers, and older people who may be forgetful or are slow and unsteady in their movements.

Burns can be shallow, only affecting the outer layer of skin; these are minor burns if they only affect a small area. They can be deeper, causing blisters to form and showing the same signs as above, or very deep, damaging all layers of the skin and even parts underneath.

Key signs

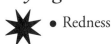 • Redness

• Pain
• Swelling- these are the shallow burns.

• Blisters with surrounding raw skin – these are deeper burns.
• Pale, waxy often scorched skin – these are very deep burns.

Special points to note about burns and scalds

Burns and scalds can cause shock because they destroy the body's waterproof skin layer, letting body fluid leak out – this is shown by the blisters. When a large area is involved, shock is greater and the person's life is in danger.

This type of injury also destroys the skin's natural ability to defend the body against microbes and infection. Body cells will go on burning for a time after the person gets away from the heat unless the area of skin is cooled down.

What to do

 1 With a very deep burn, send for medical help immediately.
2 With an extensive burn, send for medical help as well – see below about deciding on

this.

3 Cool the area with lots of cold water. Do this for at least 10 minutes. If a limb is affected, immerse all the burned area in a sink or bath; if part of the chest or trunk then pour on water with the person lying down.

4 Check breathing and circulation while you are doing this, resuscitate if necessary.

5 Carefully remove or loosen any tight jewellery or clothing before the area swells up.

6 Cover the burned area with a sterile dressing, clean cloth or clingfilm to prevent infection. Plastic bags are useful for hands and feet.

What not to do

 1 Never remove anything which is sticking to the burn.

2 Never handle the damaged area.

3 Never apply any 'remedies' to the burn e.g. witchhazel, butter, ointment etc.

4 Never burst blisters.

5 Never use fluffy coverings.

6 Never attach dressings to damaged skin.

If you can, estimate how much skin is involved if the burn is shallow or the deeper (blistered) type. Do not spend much time on this – if you cannot do it, and it is more than the area you can cover with your hand, get medical help.

The area of the body's surface can be divided into percentage areas of 9%. The diagram in Figure 37 shows you how. If a hand area is involved, then get medical help. If a '9% area' is involved, the person should be taken to hospital as shock is likely to occur. If the person has a very deep burn – hospital without delay e.g. by ambulance or car. If in doubt, get to hospital as soon as possible.

Children and babies can have a large area of their skin burned or scalded by a relatively small accident because they are so small. Only treat very minor burns yourself.

Remember, burns can have many causes which can be dangerous to you such as fires, electricity, chemicals etc. always check your own safety in such events – do not make more victims! Any burn involving the air passages, including the mouth may cause the patient to suffocate and needs special treatment in hospital without delay.

ELECTRIC SHOCK

When a person comes into contact with an electrical current we say they get an electric

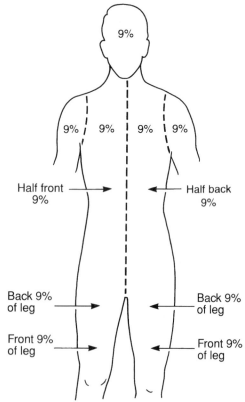

Figure 55   *Percentage areas of the body important in the treatment of burns*

shock. This can happen in any care setting which has unsafe or faulty electrical equipment, flexes to appliances which have become frayed or unguarded or overloaded electrical connection points. Children are particularly at risk, as in most homes electric sockets are near the ground and they are likely to poke things into any unguarded holes. Older people may not check their electrical equipment very often and forget about safe procedures, so once again this is a hazard for everybody to guard against, but care settings for the young and the old especially.

Key signs

- Victim will be badly shaken or even unconscious.
- Breathing and heart action may stop.
- Electrical burns (often deep burns) where the current has entered and left the skin.
- Signs of shock – rapid pulse, cold clammy (damp) grey skin, feeling sick and thirsty.

It is important to note that if you touch the casualty with bare hands while the current is still flowing through the victim, you will also experience electric shock. If the area is wet, the chances of electric shock are greater. This is why there are no electric points in bathrooms, only pull switches. Remember, electricity and water are very dangerous together.

What to do

1 Switch off the current at the quickest point.
2 Then, and only then, check breathing and pulses, resuscitating if necessary.
3 Cool any burns (see procedure under burns).

4 Place in the recovery position and send for emergency medical services.
5 If apparently unharmed, rest and call the doctor to check over.

If for any reason you cannot switch off the current, you can try to knock the victim away from the source of electricity using a broomhandle, chair or similar *wooden* material. Never use anything metal which will conduct electricity through you. Make sure you are standing on raised wood, plastic rubber or thick paper to insulate your body from the source. Only do this as a last resort, it is very dangerous for you.

CHOKING

This occurs when an object gets stuck at the back of the throat and block the air passages. Objects are usually food, sweets and small toys. Obviously, care settings for young children are particularly likely, but choking is fairly common in older people who may not chew their food properly and have weaker muscles.

Key signs

- Victim suddenly grasps throat or coughs violently.
- Voice affected – may have difficulty in speaking.
- Breathing becomes gasping and troublesome.
- Skin colour, particularly lips, may look blue.

What to do

1 Bend the victim until the head is lower that the chest.

2 Give several hard slaps with a flat hand between the shoulder blades, use less force for a child and even less for a baby.

3 If this fails to remove the blockage, and the victim is an adult or older child try the abdominal thrust. Standing behind the victim, lock your hands together under the rib cage at the front and pull sharply inwards and upwards against the chest. Your hands should have the fingers locked into one another, one hand palm up and the other palm down. Try this four or five times and if it does not unblock the air passages repeat back slaps and thrusts alternately about five times each.

4 If the victim becomes unconscious begin resuscitation and send for the emergency medical services.

Several people have died because they started to choke and ran to the bathroom, often people laughed at them. Follow someone who is choking and help in the way described above. It is not a laughing matter and can be a serious medical emergency.

Do not give abdominal thrusts to a baby, and only perform this on a child if you are sure you know what to do, otherwise begin resuscitation.

BROKEN BONES

These are also called fractures. In children, fractures of bones may not be complete but cracks similar to that obtained if you bend a green branch of a bush or tree. Such breaks are 'greenstick' fractures, and occur because a child's bones are more bendable than adults'. Older people have more brittle or less solid bones than younger adults and their bones break more easily. Fractures, particularly of the arm or hip, are more common in care settings for older people, who are unsteady and more likely to fall.

Key signs

● Recent knock or fall.

● Pain at the site of injury.
● Swelling and often bruising.
● Deformity.
● There may be signs of shock, particularly if a major bone is broken.

What to do

1 Support and hold the injured part.
2 Tie to a rigid part of the body e.g. arm in sling to chest, damaged leg to good leg. Always tie from the joint above the injury to the joint below the injury to stop movement. Pad all bony lumps with soft padding e.g. between knees and ankles.
3 If the fracture is known as an open fracture, which means there is an open wound in the skin, any bleeding must first be controlled by direct pressure over a pad (however, do not press on bone ends) – see section on cuts. Pad well with cotton wool and bandage. If bone ends are protruding build up the area with non fluffy material such as gauze pads before bandaging over the pads. Make the area unable to move as described before.
4 Send for the emergency service.
5 Make sure you do not bandage so tightly that blood flow is partly blocked or stopped. You can test this by pressing on a finger or toenail until it goes white, then releasing the pressure and checking to see if the pink colour returns. If it does not the bandage is too tight.

6 Keep the client still unless he/she is in danger, do not move them until the broken bone is fixed.

7 Prevent the client from eating or drinking in case he/she has to have an operation.

CUTS

Cuts or wounds can happen anywhere to any person. They may be cuts from a blade or sharp edge which bleed a lot but heal well, or tears of the skin which bleed less, take a longer time to heal and are likely to become infected.

Key signs

- Bleeding
- Pain
- Break in the skin surface.

What to do

1 Wash your hands quickly but thoroughly in hot soapy water before and after dealing with the cut.

2 Stop bleeding by raising the part (or lowering the rest of the body) and apply direct pressure to the wound edges. Safety point – you should protect yourself against contact with body fluids of another person if you possibly can. Wear disposable gloves or put your hands inside clean plastic bags, cover any sores or breaks in your own skin with dressings, apply the pressure over a dressing or clean cloth. You will also be protecting the victim from any infection you may be carrying as well.

3 Put on a sterile dressing or clean cloth over any other material you may have used. If the blood comes through, put another dressing on top of the old one.

4 Check for any other injuries.

5 If the cut is deep, long, dirty, fails to stop bleeding, or you suspect other injuries, get medical help as soon as possible.

6 Be aware that shock can develop quickly if much blood is lost and send the client to hospital without waiting.

7 Watch the patient carefully for signs of lowered consciousness – confusion, not answering question, groaning, flickering of eyelids etc. – place in recovery position after stopping bleeding, monitor pulse, breathing and patient's responses to you.

8 Treat for shock if help is delayed and bleeding is considerable, by raising legs, lowering head and covering patient with a blanket.

Basic first aid procedures

You will need to be able to describe the key signs and the correct things to do for a person who has stopped breathing, is unconscious and has no pulses. You have already learned about choking, scalding and bleeding. You should know when, and how, to call the emergency services.

Assess any emergency first, but do not agonise over your decisions. If in doubt at all, then send for the emergency services. You will definitely need to request the emergency services if you are involved in cases of:

- Unconsciousness
- Absence of pulses or breathing
- Difficulty with breathing
- Bleeding unless it is minor
- Fractures of the skull, back or legs
- Severe burns and scalds
- Actual or suspected heart attack

- Suspected poisoning and drug overdose
- Clinical shock

This is not a full list of injuries that need hospital treatment, for example other fractures will need to be seen by doctors, but do not necessarily need an ambulance if a car and driver are available.

Find a place where you or someone else can use a telephone to dial 999; it does not have to be a telephone box, a large number of people carry mobile phones and houses, shops, garages and public houses all have telephones. Dialling 999 is a free service so you do not have to find the right coins to make the call. The operator will ask which service you require, you may only need the ambulance service, but think quickly whether you need the police or fire services as well. If it is a serious road accident, you might need all three! The operator will ask which telephone number you are calling from, if you are "cut off" they can trace the call; the number is usually found on the box or dial, but a mobile is hidden, you will need to ask the owner. You

will then be connected to the ambulance control officer, assuming you have asked for an ambulance, and s/he will ask you where the emergency is, what is the matter, how many people are involved and their condition. They will also need to know if there are risks such as live electricity, fire, smoke, chemical fumes etc. Listen carefully to the person at the other end as they might give you special instructions to follow and tell you how long the ambulance will take to reach you. When you have finished the call, hang up or switch off correctly and organise lookouts or lights to help the ambulance crew find you. This is particularly important if you are in a place far away from roads and houses.

Cardio-pulmonary resuscitation

RESUSCITATION

When looking at the 'what to do' sections of several emergencies, there has been the need to resuscitate. Now, let us look at the ways in

Figure 56

which you could do this. However, it cannot be emphasised often enough that you really cannot learn this on your own.

You need special equipment and a trained person to teach you and tell you when you are doing it correctly. When a casualty is not breathing and is turning bluish-grey you must get some oxygen from your breath into their chest as soon as possible. Approximately 20% of the air around us is oxygen, when we have breathed this in and used some of the oxygen, there is still 16% left. Enough to support another person, so this is why mouth to mouth resuscitation works.

You cannot try this with another breathing person, so 'emergency' technology has provided us with dummies or, more correctly, manikins on which to practice. Manikins usually have the facility of inflatable chests and compressible hearts. They are quite expensive so you will have to join a first aid class if you do not have one available for your use.

With the casualty flat on their back, your first aim is to open the person's air passages. Put one hand under the person's neck and the other on their forehead, while gently tilting backwards until the nostrils point to the sky. Taking care sweep your finger around the casualty's mouth to remove any obstruction.

Close the casualty's nose by pinching the nostrils with the thumb and forefinger.

Take a breath for yourself and seal your mouth around the casualty's mouth. As you blow gently but firmly into their mouth watch to see if the chest rises, take your mouth away to breathe for yourself and watch the chest fall. Repeat the process 10 times to load up their lungs with oxygen. Check that the pulse is still there. If you can, call or telephone for help between series of 10 breaths, checking the pulse at these intervals as well. If you are doing

it properly, you should begin to see a change in colour, particularly in the lips and tongue.

If the colour does not improve check the way that you are doing it, especially opening the airway, and that the pulse is present. If the chest is failing to rise, check your airway position, your mouth seal, nose blocked off correctly and any obstruction is cleared. Continue until the casualty begins to breathe on their own (then place in recovery position and check regularly), or expert help arrives. Your rate should be approximately 15 breaths each minute.

Young children and babies

Aged four and under, lie child along arm and seal mouth around child's mouth *and* nose give short, gentle breaths about 20/minute.

When there is no pulse

If the heart stops pumping blood around the body, you will have to be the pump until expert

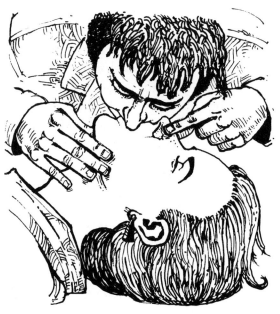

Figure 57   *Mouth-to-mouth resuscitation*

help arrives or the heart starts again. The oxygen needs to be carried to the body in general, and brain in particular. On the other hand, a person's heart may be pumping blood, but they have stopped breathing, in which case, the heart will soon stop due to lack of oxygen.

In both these emergencies mouth to mouth resuscitation will need to be combined with chest compression and the two techniques together are known as cardio – pulmonary resuscitation or CPR.

CHEST COMPRESSION

First, check the carotid pulse (not the wrist pulse) which is one of two large arteries lying on either side of the windpipe in the neck. Feel with two fingers pressed deep into the side of the neck (see Figure 58).

If the carotid pulse is absent this means that the heart is not working and you must commence chest compression immediately.

External chest compressions, if correctly performed, will artificially pump about one-third of the body's blood around the circulation, and if this is oxygenated it will keep the casualty alive for the time being.

The method traps the heart between the vertebral column at the back and the rib cage/breastbone at the front and this expels blood from the heart towards the lungs and into the main artery (the aorta). As the pressure is released more blood is sucked into the heart from the big veins supplying it.

METHOD OF CHEST COMPRESSION

The pressure must be applied to the correct place for success. Feel for the notch at the base of the neck between the two collar bones and also for the notch where the ribs meet in the centre at the bottom of the rib cage. Find the halfway point between these two notches, then find the halfway mark of the lowest of these halves.

Kneeling beside the casualty at the level of your marked spot, place the heel of your hand on this point and the heel of your other hand on top interlocking the fingers together. The heel of your hand is the muscular bit above the wrist at the bottom of the palm.

Lean forwards over the casualty with straight arms and push firmly down until the chest is compressed at least four to five centimetres then releasing. Keep the actual fingers off the chest only using the heel of the lowest hand and do not move the hands in between compressions. You must aim for sixty to eighty pumps/minute (more for children and babies). Experts agree that to help you keep to time, it is useful to say one and two and three and four, up to fifteen, then begin again.

BEFORE CPR

Before you start CPR (but do not delay for long – remember the brain cannot work without oxygen for more than three minutes) try to shout or 'phone for help. CPR is exhausting and if you are on your own you may not be able to continue for long.

ON YOUR OWN

Carry out two breaths then fifteen chest compressions followed by two breaths, fifteen compressions and so on. Do not stop to check pulses until you see some sign of blood circulation. If the heart begins again, check breathing – continue mouth to mouth if absent. If present, place in recovery position and check both every three minutes.

WITH ANOTHER HELPER

First helper goes for help while second begins CPR as above. When they return, one at head ventilating the lungs and one working on heart compression is the most usual. One breath is given after every five compressions of the chest. Monitor as above.

Exchange tasks every few minutes so that you can keep it up for longer. This time the 'breathing' person can check the pulse as well, every few minutes.

Remember, do not practice on a living person. Do join a class and get trained properly in the techniques.

ASSESSMENT EVIDENCE

For a pass grade, you will need to demonstrate the procedure for cardio-pulmonary resuscitation on a mannikin (doll) specially designed for that purpose. You must <u>never</u> do this on a healthy person! If you have special needs and cannot do this yourself, you will need to be able to correctly instruct someone else to do this.

If you are trying for a merit grade, you will also need to demonstrate summoning the emergency services and placing an individual in the recovery position.

If you are trying for a distinction grade, you will need to show your assessor that you can demonstrate accurately a range of first aid procedures and explain what you might do if a person has more than one type of emergency. Remember that you will carry out the most important procedure for saving life **first**. For example, you will not try to stop bleeding if a person has no pulses and is not breathing, it would be a waste of time as they would die. The golden rule is ABC airway, breathing and circulation, then attend to other injuries such as bleeding or fractures.

If you have a current first aid qualification, show this to your tutor and she will give you credit for this part of the unit.

While you are studying this unit, why not take a first aid qualification as well? The emergency aid for appointed persons certificate would serve you very well for this unit. As there are other emergencies that are not part of this unit, you will not be able to say that you are qualified in first aid as a result of achieving this unit.

Student activity

- Find a partner and practise counting and recording the number of beats or pulses occurring in one minute, using your fingers lightly placed on the pulse. Do not use your thumb as it has a pulse of its own and you could be counting your own pulse instead of your partner's! Try to get used to the rhythm and strength of the beats after you have counted them. How will you record pulse beats if you are monitoring someone's pulse?
- Carry out a little physical exercise, such as running up and down steps a few times, waving your arms about or something similar and repeat the counting. What has happened to the pulse rate? This can also happen with raised body temperature, anaemia and loss of blood. Other conditions can do the opposite.
- If you can, try taking a child's or baby's pulse. This is much more difficult and may take a few attempts to count accurately. A minute seems a long time to count a pulse for, and can be tiring if you are doing it for some time. An easier way is to count for fifteen or thirty seconds and multiply by either four or

Figure 58   Neck and wrist pulse points

two, to get the pulse rate in sixty seconds or one minute. Try this now.

- Find out what is the usual normal range of pulse rate for an adult, a child of about eight years of age and a young baby.

Student activity

 • Why not repeat activity 13, but this time as well as counting pulse, count breaths as well, at rest and doing moderate and hard physical exercise. You can collect all the figures together – called data – and make a table to present your results. You could calculate the mean using the formula below.

$$\text{Mean} = \frac{\text{all the numbers for the same thing added together}}{\text{the number of numbers for that thing}}$$

- For example, a class group found that their resting pulse rates were 69, 76, 67, 70, 72, 65, 72, 69 beats every minute. When these are added together they make 560, but there are 8 numbers in the row, so the mean is 560 ÷ 8, this is 70 beats per minute. You could calculate mean pulses and breathing rates at rest and after exercise. (Application of Number 1.3.)

Student activity

 • Take your own carotid pulse, by counting for fifteen seconds and multiplying it by four. Now take a friend's or a relative's carotid pulse to get practice in feeling for it.

Student activity

 • Ask your teacher to show you a skeleton and a heart model. Find the place where the heart should be inside the chest and carry out the measuring described under 'Method of Chest Compression' on page 92.

Student activity

 • Role play a selected number of health emergencies, describing what you are looking for and what you would do in those circumstances. Different groups could act out several different emergencies and the audience ask them questions. The role plays could be videoed for evidence.

- Alternatively, let each group investigate an emergency and present their findings to the rest of the group. They can then answer the audience's questions and evaluate the learning activity at the end.

- Students could write personal reports of other groups' presentations and include the notes and visual displays for their own evidence.

Self-check questions

 1 List the safety procedures you should take when you are called to a case of electric shock.

2 Describe what happens when you dial 999 in an emergency.

3 Which group of clients is more likely to suffer greenstick fractures?

4 Explain what you would do if a client in your work placement suffered an epileptic fit.

5 How would you care for a member of your class who develops asthma?

6 What is the difference between a burn and a scald?

7 Describe what is meant by an abdominal thrust and say when it would be used.

8 Under what circumstances would you call the emergency services?

9 What would you do if a member of your class burned two fingertips?

10 A client has banged his head and was 'out' for a few seconds. What would you do?

ASSESSMENT EVIDENCE

You need to produce a demonstration of your understanding of common hazards and health emergencies, which includes:

- a workplace safety survey (audit)
- explaining what may happen if you fail to follow correct health and safety practice
- demonstrating some first-aid procedures

To achieve a pass you must show you can:	To achieve a merit you must also show you can:	To achieve a distinction you must also show you can:
• correctly identify basic hazards and health and safety features in your survey (audit)	• accurately identify and describe the location of hazards and a range of health and safety features	• relate the location and type of health and safety features identified in your survey (audit) to the hazards, and draw valid conclusions about how they help reduce risks
• correctly identify possible immediate effects of failure to follow correct health and safety practice	• understand and explain clearly procedures for dealing with health emergencies	• make realistic suggestions for improvements you have identified in your survey
• safely demonstrate (or correctly instruct*) cardio-pulmonary resuscitation procedures	• accurately demonstrate (or instruct*) basic first-aid procedures, relating correct symptoms and procedures	• competently demonstrate (or instruct*) a range of first-aid procedures, explaining what you might need to do if a person had more than one symptom

*to be used where you are unable to physically demonstrate the skills. You should talk another person through the correct procedures.

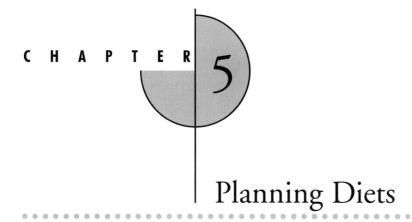

Planning Diets

CONTENTS AND LINKS

More and more research shows us that the pattern of food we eat is linked to our health. It is not only the type of food that matters, but the quantities as well. A healthy mix of foods in the right amounts to keep us healthy is known as a balanced diet. You have already learned some basic information about food types in unit 2 (Understanding health and well-being) and some key principles of food hygiene in unit 4 (Investigating common hazards and emergencies). In this unit, you will build your information up from this learning so that you can plan diets to meet different people's needs and safely prepare some simple courses. Many workers in care settings are involved in food serving, preparation, cooking or planning menus and many young people get paid jobs in the food industry, even if it is only casual employment to earn some money. This unit will be useful for those reasons as well as looking after yourself and eventually your family.

You will learn that a healthy balanced diet has the correct balance of food from the five main food groups and how to use food tables. You will need to know the roles of the main parts of food and their sources; this will help you to plan different meals for different people. Finally, you will the basic rules for preparing and presenting meals so that they are safe for people to eat and look appetising. Ill people often have poor appetites and they can easily be put off eating a meal they need because it is poorly presented.

A HEALTHY DIET

In unit 2, you learned that there are three food chemicals called proteins, carbohydrates and fats. These are the foods that are energy-rich and make up a large part of your meal. They are often called macronutrients; macro means large and a nutrient is a substance that provides you with raw materials for living. You also learned of the sources of these chemicals such as meat, fish, cheese, eggs, peas and beans supply protein.

Figure 59   *Protein assists growth of body tissues including muscles*

Protein foods as you can see are the foods that cost a lot of money, so it is important to have enough protein for your daily needs, but not a lot more as they are broken down by the liver and parts are used for energy. As we have other foods to supply energy, this is rather wasteful.

Your body consists of millions of tiny cells, far too small to see with the naked eye; a large part of each cell is protein – you could think of cells as watery bags of protein. You won't be at all surprised now to learn that the job of animal or vegetable proteins in your diet is to make your new cells, in other words, growth and mend damaged cells. You could think of proteins as the bricks that build your body. Many hormones are also made of protein and so are chemicals that are responsible for making your blood clot, carry oxygen in your blood and digesting your food. About 20% of your diet should be protein.

Carbohydrate food

This includes all the starchy and sugary food that you eat, including potatoes, rice, pasts, jams, sweets, bread, cakes and so on. This should be the main part of any meal as it supplies us with our energy to do work. Not work like school or college work, although that is included, but cellular work such as using our muscles, to walk and run, pumping the blood around our bodies, breathing, processing our food and many more. You need a lot of energy to keep you going throughout the day and it is the main job of carbohydrate to supply that energy. Energy is a difficult thing to describe, but you could think of it as stored work. Most people these days have cereal or toast for breakfast and these are very important carbohydrates as they provide you with energy to start your day. If you are a person who does not have breakfast, maybe just a cold or hot drink, try eating cereal or toast,

Figure 60   *Cereal gives you energy to start your day off right!*

you will find that you can go about your day with more energy and not need to tuck into fatty foods at lunchtime!

Some experts on eating called nutritionists will say that breakfast is the most important meal of the day. However, you do need carbohydrate with every meal and it is traditional in most countries to eat potatoes, bread, rice or maize as the main part of a meal. These carbohydrates are all starchy foods and are much better for you than the sugars, they take longer to digest, fill you up and also contain fibre. Sugars such as those in sweets and convenience foods make your blood sugar rise quickly, but equally soon make it fall again, and you feel hungry more quickly. They also can cause tooth decay. Sugar in fruit and vegetables is much better for you. About 60% of your meals should be carbohydrate.

Fats

All of us hear a lot about fats in our diet and nearly all of it is bad news!

However, fats are an essential part of our diet and we need to take 20% of our diet as fat. The big trouble is – fats make meals more interesting, make meals softer and quicker to eat and we consume far too much of them. Most convenience food are heavily loaded with fat, and even though some may be labelled with 50% fat or healthy option, they can still have considerable fat in them. It has to be said that there is still a lot of argument over fat in our diet, particularly in relation to heart attacks and strokes, but it does make sense to cut down if you eat a lot of fried food, chocolate, cream, butter and convenience foods.

Fat also gives us energy, but it gives **twice** as much for every gram eaten as carbohydrates; eat a lot of fatty foods and you soon become overweight. Fat also helps to make some hormones, store vitamins, insulate us against the cold weather and protect organs against bumps and knocks. Like protein, 20% of our diet should be fat.

The following pie chart shows the percentage of macronutrients in a balanced diet.

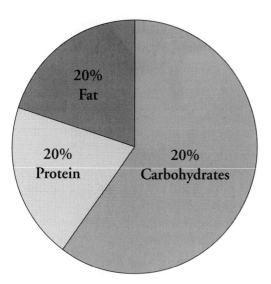

Fibre or roughage

When you eat plant material such as peas, beans, lettuce, cabbage you are eating plant cells. Plant cells have a different structure to animal cells and their outer walls are made up of a carbohydrate called cellulose. Humans cannot digest cellulose that is also known as fibre, roughage or bran. They are all words for the same thing. However, fibre is of great benefit to us as it passes through our digestive system it absorbs water and swells up. This makes:

- bulky motions that are easy to pass (prevents constipation)
- makes us feel full for longer so we eat less
- helps to prevent bowel disorders such as cancer and colitis.

Fibre will not have any other jobs inside the body, as it doesn't get absorbed. It passes in through the mouth and out through the back passage or anus.

Two important groups of food chemicals that you did not learn about in unit 2 are vitamins and minerals. These are important to our health but are only needed in very small amounts each day and do not supply us with energy. They are called the micronutrients (micro means tiny).

Vitamins

The main vitamins you should know about are vitamins A, C, and D. There are a large number of vitamins under the label B, such as vitamin B1, B6 and B12, but this is a complex group and if you take enough cereals, liver, kidney and green vegetables you would have all the requirements. Vitamins A and D are both fat-soluble vitamins and found in milk, cream and butter. Yellow/orange vegetables like carrots, peppers and tomatoes are also rich in sources of Vitamin A, while fish liver oils are rich in Vitamin D. Nowadays, breakfast cereals have some vitamins added, particularly A and D. Vitamin A helps you to see in the dark and helps to keep us healthy Vitamin D is important in the absorption of calcium, a mineral salt essential for healthy teeth and bones. When children do not get enough Vitamin D they develop a condition called rickets, where bones bend easily under the weight of the body and both cartilage and bone are not formed properly. Vitamin C (and the Bs) are water soluble vitamins. Vitamin C helps wounds to heal, broken bones to mend and stops the mouth and gums from getting sore in a disease called scurvy. Fresh fruit and vegetables contain Vitamin C with oranges, lemons, blackcurrants and strawberries being particularly rich. A few years ago, there was a potato shortage in this country and prices became very high; elderly people were discovered to be suffering from scurvy that year and for the first time nutritionists realised how much Vitamin C elderly people were getting from potatoes.

Vitamins are essential to healthy living, because they help bodily processes to work properly, they do not supply energy or raw material for our bodies.

Mineral salts

Although there are several mineral salts needed in our diets in such tiny amounts they are called traces, you will learn about two of the most crucial salts, iron and calcium. Iron is needed to make the special red pigment in blood that is needed to carry vital oxygen to the cells. Without enough iron in your diet, you will develop a condition called anaemia, in which you are tired and breathless when you exercise such as going up the stairs. Women and girls are more likely to develop anaemia because of the loss of blood from menstruation. Pregnant women need more iron to make the extra special pigment for their developing babies. Iron is found in red meat, liver, spinach (remember Popeye!)

watercress and other green vegetables like broccoli and okra.

Calcium

Whenever you think of calcium imagine it linked to Vitamin D because the two are inseparable. Calcium is very difficult to absorb as it does not dissolve in water easily. Imagine trying to dissolve a piece of schoolroom chalk, which is made of mineral salts, in a cup of water, it forms sludge at the bottom of the cup. It is calcium that makes both bones and teeth hard so that the body weight can be supported and hard foods broken up. Vitamin D can be thought of as the magic that helps calcium along into the water of the blood. Calcium is found in milk, cheese and fish and rib bones. Vinegar is an acid and partly dissolves calcium from fish and ribs, it is used to make sweet and sour sauce over spare ribs. Complete the following table:

Dietary need	Sources	Purpose
protein		growth and repair of damaged cells
fats		supplies energy insulates against heat loss
carbohydrate	bread, rice, pasta, cakes, sweets, jam butter, margarine, cheese, chocolate, eggs	
vitamin A		essential to life and helps seeing in the dark
vitamin C		helps wounds to heal and prevents scurvy
vitamin D	milk, cheese, fish, liver, oils	
iron		
calcium		hardens bones and teeth
water	orange juice, tea, coca cola, melon	

Table 5.1   *Main components of diet, their sources and functions*

The last ingredient of a diet is the one that people could not survive without – water.

Water

You have already met things dissolving like calcium and water soluble vitamins and others getting in to blood, bone and body cells. Water is the main component of our body cells, blood and urine and other substances dissolve in it to be carried around the body. You should drink about 1.5 litres of water every day and more in hot weather to make up for the loss in sweat. Fruit juices, tea, soup and all the other watery foods are classed as water, but drinking plain water is good for you also. Solid foods, even a digestive biscuit also contain a little water. Some fruits, like melon, contain a lot of water too.

You have now learned about the seven parts of diet and to revise this why not copy out the table on page 101 and complete the missing boxes.

You will be able to refer quickly to your table as you do your assessment task. You have learned the main parts of food, where they can be found (the sources) and what their purpose in the body is. You know which

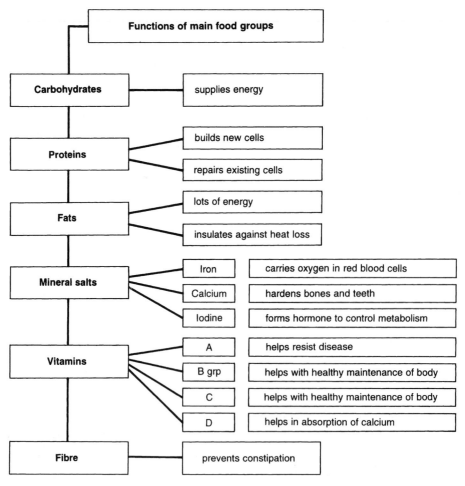

Figure 61   *Functions of main food groups*

types compose most of your meal and which types you need only small amounts for.

To make it easy for people to understand nutrition, experts have divided food into groups by their nature and have said that something from each food group should be eaten every day. You will find a diagram of these food groups in Figure 61.

To help people further, 8 guidelines on healthy, balanced diets are listed below. You should use these as a checklist when or after you have planned your diet.

Guidelines for a healthy, balanced diet

- enjoy your food
- eat a variety of different foods
- eat the right amount of food to be a healthy weight
- eat plenty of foods that are rich in starch and fibre
- don't eat too much fat
- don't eat sugary foods too often
- make sure there are enough vitamins and minerals in your food
- if you drink alcohol, keep within recommended limits.

Different people's needs

It is obvious that people will need different amounts and types of food. Children will eat less than adults, we all know that, but adolescents need more food than elderly people, pregnant women have special requirements compared to other women and so on.

AGE

Very young babies need 5 or 6 meals of small amounts of milk (either breast-milk or for-mula milk), as the amount to satisfy them increases the number of feed drops to 4. This is continued until the child is weaned and starts taking solid foods. Small, soft foods first (about half a cupful) again slowly increasing and taking in one different taste at a time. By the age of two or three, the child is taking the same meals as the family, although smaller in quantity, with the exception of salads and chops and similar foods. Meals gradually increase in size and complexity, but at adolescence, when there is a huge growth spurt, teenagers can be eating more than most adults. Older people usually take smaller amounts again and may have trouble chewing harder foods.

SEX

Apart from a small period of 3 to 4 years during early adolescence, males require larger amounts of food than females. They tend to be taller and heavier and do not have so much fat so lose body heat more readily.

PHYSICAL ACTIVITY

Using muscles requires a lot of energy, so it follows that the more active a person is the more food they will require. This should be mainly as starchy foods (see earlier notes on carbohydrates). A typist sitting at a desk all the working day requires a lot less food than a builder's labourer who is carrying heavy bricks and mixing concrete among other things. Athletes need a lot of carbohydrate, much more so than someone who may be unemployed and lounges around watching TV. You will need to take notice of the type of employment or recreational activities of the person for whom you plan your meals.

Why should a diet be balanced? What happens if someone doesn't eat a balanced diet over a long period of time?

The most obvious external thing you might notice is incorrect weight. The person might be either overweight or underweight. They would tend to have poor physical health, more tiredness, be unwilling to exert themselves, poor skin, more likely to catch infections and a general lack of vitality and health. There would be an increased risk of developing bowel disorders and heart disease if they consumed diets rich in fat and lacking in fibre. You have also learned about scurvy, rickets and anaemia if diets are lacking in certain vitamins and minerals.

People's choices

CULTURE AND RELIGION

Not all people eat the same choice of food. Some people have racial and cultural needs and might be restricted in the foods they eat. In the table below you will find the main differences in the food eaten in some religions;

VEGETARIAN AND VEGAN DIETS

Many people in our society have chosen not to eat animal products apart from milk or cheese. They either do not like meat and fish or believe that it is cruel to slaughter animals for our food. Some vegetarians eat eggs. This might suggest that vegetarians might not take in adequate protein in their diets; however, peas, beans, soya beans, nuts, lentils and rice all contain some protein. Vegetarians must be careful to take a wide variety of plant foods in their diet to make sure of getting all the essential types of protein that they need. People who eat animal products will get this naturally, but plant proteins can have some types missing. Vegetarians also must watch out for their iron containing foods, plenty of leafy green vegetables and egg yolk will provide most of the iron requirements. Vegans avoid all animal products, even honey and milk, it is a healthy diet high in fibre and low in fat, but again a wide variety of plants must be eaten. They too can be at risk of developing anaemia and may also become short of calcium. Calcium can be supplied by tofu or soya bean curd to remedy this. People on these

Different culture and religion	Differences in food eaten
Hindu religion	no animal products at all
Judaism or Jewish religion	food has to be specially prepared and is called kosher food
	no pig products
	no meat and dairy products eaten together
	food has been drained of blood
Muslim religion	no pig products
	food has been drained of blood
	no alcohol

diets can, if necessary, take iron, vitamin B_{12} and calcium substitutes available from any high street chemist.

WEIGHT GAIN OR WEIGHT LOSS DIETS

Some people need to alter their weight up or down; this may be through personal choice or on medical advice.

If food intake is greater than the amount of energy used, the energy will be stored as glycogen (a carbohydrate) in liver and muscles or as fat around organs and underneath the skin. Over a period of time, this leads to an increase in body weight and the person may decide to start a weight reducing diet. This can be effective for some people, but for many, it is very difficult and they give up. The weight gain is usually over many years, but people will expect to lose significant amounts of weight in a matter of weeks or a few months. The most helpful way of planning a weight reducing diet is to combine it with an exercise programme and cut down the amount of fat and sugar eaten. Changing the way food is prepared and eaten will help in the following ways:

- grill food instead of frying
- choose leaner cuts of meat and remove any obvious fat
- eat plenty of fibre containing foods to fill you up
- limit convenience foods such as burgers and chips
- change chocolate bars and puddings for apples or similar fresh fruit
- cut out snacks such as crisps and nuts.

Do not forget that people on weight reducing diets still need protein, vitamins and minerals. People who need to put on more weight should still remember the healthy guidelines, but can eat more fat and carbohydrates than the rest of us. If they cannot eat large meals, then smaller meals more often is an acceptable way to do it. Milky drinks at bedtime, cereal, toast and a boiled egg for breakfast and so on.

People in different client groups

You need to know how dietary requirements differ for children, pregnant women and older people.

CHILDREN

You have already learned a little bit about children's diets, but some foods are really important in childhood. Protein requirements are larger for every kilogram of body weight then adults, because new cells are being made every day of a child's life in the process of growth. More blood cells are needed with growing so iron is an important item and our two inseparable friends again calcium and Vitamin D for growing bones and teeth. Children are only still when they are asleep, so they need plenty of carbohydrate to supply the energy for movement. Other food items are still necessary of course, but extra supplies of those mentioned are needed.

PREGNANT WOMEN

All requirements for children are necessary for the pregnant woman – after all, she has a child growing inside her. She also requires a good supply of some of the B vitamins to guard against some congenital defects (defects in the formation of the infant). She does not need to eat for two as a lot of extra weight can be harmful in pregnancy, as well as being difficult to lose after the birth. A good balanced

Age	Energy req. kJ		Protein req. g	Calcium mg	Iron mg	Vit A µg	Vit C mg	Vit D µg
	Male	Female						
1	5000	4500	30	27	600	600	7	7
	20	20	10	10				
2	5750	5500	35	32	600	600	7	7
	20	20	10	10				
3–4	6500	6250	39	37	600	600	8	8
	20	20	10	10				
5–6	7250	7000	43	42	600	600	10	10
	20	20	10	10				
7–8	8250	8000	49	48	600	600	10	10
	20	20	–					
9–11	9500	8500	56	51	700	700	12	12
	25	25	–					
12–14	11000	9000	66	53	700	700	12	12
	25	25	–					
15–17	12000	9000	72	53	600	600	12	12
	30	30	–					

Table 5.2   *Nutritional requirements of children per day*

diet with plenty of protein, dairy foods, fruit and vegetables is required.

OLDER PEOPLE

Generally, people over 65 years of age are not as active as younger people and require less in quantity, but not in quality. It is still important for older people to get plenty of fibre, vitamins and minerals, less fat and some protein and carbohydrate. They are not growing, but they need protein for repair and replacement of cells and carbohydrate for energy. They may need softer foods that can easily be cut up, but even apples can be stewed or cut into tiny pieces. Food labels show the amount of energy, protein, carbohydrate and fat in the food and often the vitamins and minerals as well. Get into the habit of reading labels on the food you eat. You will find them very useful. Energy is measured in kilojules or kilocalories (an older measurement), but this is of little use to you unless you know the energy levels normal for different people. It is impossible to remember all the different figures for different people, but if you know the figure for an adult male who is moderately active, you can use common sense to get the rest.

An average adult male needs 12,500 kilojoules (kJ) every day. We know women require less than men, so about 10,000kL for a woman, and about 9-10,000kJ for an older man. Teenagers going through puberty need as much as an adult man, so about 12-12,500kJ. Pregnant woman and those who are breast-feeding nearly as much as an adult man so 12,000kJ. So, if you learn one figure, you can get as near as you need for the others. When you look at either food labels or food tables, the amounts of different things are usually given for 100 grams of the food. You will need to find out what 100 gram portions look like. An example of a food table is given in Table 5.3, your tutor will have copies of food tables or you can find them in the library. The easiest ones to follow are those published by the Ministry of Agriculture, Fisheries and Food. They also publish inexpensive booklets on:

- healthy eating for older people
- healthy diets for infants and young children
- the balance of good health
- Manual of Nutrition.

Student activities

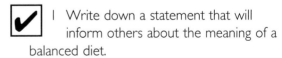 1 As a class group, each person brings 3 foods and you weigh out 100g of each to find what this quantity looks and feels in your hand. Make a chart to say what a normal position would weigh. For instance, would an average portion of creamed or mashed potatoes be 100, 200 or 300 grams.
2 See if you can estimate the energy requirements for the following categories
- 75-year-old woman
- 8-year-old boy
- very athletic 25-year-old man
- 33-year-old mother of two babies, one is still breastfed
3 Obtain one or two samples of weight reducing diets from magazines.

- In groups of two or three discuss each diet in terms of its effectiveness and nutritional value.
- Write up your discussion or ask your tutor to video tape the session for evidence.
- Interview one or two people who follow vegetarian and vegan diets, ask them to supply a list of the foods they eat regularly.
- Discuss any nutritional problems that might have had and how they have overcome them, or how they avoid nutritional problems by careful meal planning.
- If your interviewees do not plan carefully and have not experienced nutritional problems, investigate their daily diets and draw conclusions yourself.
4 In unit 2 you were asked to complete a diary of your food intake for one week; take one of those days and using food tables find out if you took the right amount of energy for that day. If not, what might happen to your weight and health if this pattern of eating was typical and occurring over a long period of time.
5 Carry out the same exercise as in 4, but this time check for vitamins A, C, D, iron and calcium. What might happen if this was typical of your food intake over a long period of time.

Self-check questions

1 Write down a statement that will inform others about the meaning of a balanced diet.

Food	Inedible waste %	Energy kcal	kJ	Protein g	Fat g	Carbohydrate (as mono-saccharide) g	Water g
Fish							
White fish, filleted	3	77	324	17.1	0.9	0	82
Cod, fried	0	235	982	19.6	14.3	7.5	57
Fish fingers, raw	0	178	749	12.6	7.5	16.1	64
Herrings, whole	46	251	1,040	16.8	20.4	0	64
Mackerel	40	282	1,170	19.0	22.9	0	5 7
pilchards, canned in tomato sauce	0	126	531	18.8	5.4	0.7	74
Sardines, canned in oil, fish only	0	217	906	23.7	18.6	0	58
Tuna in oil	0	289	1,202	22.8	22.0	0	55
Prawns, boiled	0	107	451	22.6	1.8	0	70
Eggs							
Eggs, boiled	12	147	612	12.3	10.9	0	75
Eggs, fried	0	232	961	14.1	19.5	0	63
Fats							
Butter	0	740	3,041	0.4	82.0	0	15
Lard, cooking fat, dripping	0	892	3,667	0	99.1	0	1
Low fat spread	0	366	1,506	0	40.7	0	51
Margarine, average	0	730	3,000	0.1	81.0	0	16
Cooking and salad oil	0	899	3,696	0	99.9	0	0
Preserves, etc.							
Chocolate, milk	0	529	2,214	8.4	30.3	59.4	2
Honey	0	288	1,229	0.4	0	76.4	23
Jam	0	262	1,116	0.5	0	69.2	30
Marmalade	0	261	1,114	0.1	0	69.5	28
Sugar, white	0	394	1,680	0	0	105.3	0
Syrup	0	298	1,269	0.3	0	79.0	28
Peppermints	0	392	1,670	0.5	0.7	102.2	0
Vegetables							
Aubergines	23	14	62	0.7	0	3.1	93
Baked beans	0	81	345	4.8	0.6	15.1	74
Beans, runner, boiled	1	19	83	1.9	0.2	2.7	91
Beans, red kidney, raw	0	272	1,159	22.1	1.7	45.0	11
Beans, soya, boiled	0	141	592	12.4	6.4	9.0	67
Beetroot, boiled	0	44	189	1.8	0	9.9	83
Brussels sprouts, boiled	0	18	75	2.8	0	1.7	92
Cabbage, raw	43	22	92	2.8	0	2.8	88
Cabbage boiled	0	15	66	1.7	0	2.3	93
Carrots, old	4	23	98	0.7	0	5.4	90
Cauliflower, cooked	0	9	40	1.6	0	0.8	95
Celery	27	8	36	0.9	0	1.3	94
Courgettes, raw	13	29	122	1.6	0.4	5.0	92

Table 5.3   *Composition of food per 100g*

Calcium mg	Iron mg	Sodium mg	Vitamin A (retinol equivalent) µg	Thiamin mg	Riboflavin mg	Niacin equivalent mg	Vitamin C mg
22	0.5	99	1	0.07	0.09	6.0	0
80	0.5	100	0	0.06	0.07	4.9	0
43	0.7	320	0.2	0.09	0.06	3.5	0
33	0.8	67	46	0	0.18	7.2	0
24	1.0	130	45	0.09	0.35	11.6	0
300	2.7	370	8	0.02	0.29	11.1	0
550	2.9	650	7	0.04	0.36	12.6	0
7	1.1	420	0	0.04	0.11	17.2	0
150	1.1	1,590	0	0.03	0.03	7.4	0
52	2.0	140	190	0.09	0.47	3.7	0
64	2.5	220	140	0.07	0.42	4.2	0
15	0.2	870	985	0	0	0.1	0
1	0.1	2	0	0	0	0	0
0	0	690	900	0	0	0	0
4	0.3	800	860	0	0	0.1	0
0	0	0	0	0	0	0	0
220	1.6	120	6.6	0.10	0.23	1.6	0
5	0.4	11	0	0	0.05	0.2	0
18	1.2	14	2	0	0	0	10
35	0.6	18	8	0	0	0	10
2	0	0	0	0	0	0	0
26	1.5	270	0	0	0	0	0
7	0.2	9	0	0	0	0	0
10	0.4	3	0	0.05	0.03	1.0	5
48	1.4	550	12	0.08	0.06	1.3	0
22	0.7	1	67	0.03	0.07	0.8	5
140	6.7	40	0	0.54	0.18	5.5	0
145	2.5	15	0	0.26	0.16	3.4	0
30	0.4	64	0	0.02	0.04	0.4	5
25	0.5	2	67	0.06	0.10	0.9	40
57	0.6	7	50	0.06	0.05	0.8	55
38	0.4	4	50	0.03	0.03	0.5	20
48	0.6	95	2,000	0.06	0.05	0.7	6
18	0.4	4	5	0.06	0.06	0.8	20
52	0.6	140	0	0.03	0.03	0.5	7
30	1.5	1	58	0.05	0.09	0.6	16

2 Name the macronutrients and micronutrients in food.

3 Name the functions of all the macronutrients.

4 What is the daily energy requirement for an average adult male?

5 Name 3 substances that pregnant women need in their diet in greater amounts than normal.

6 Complete the following table, the first one is done for you.

Name of food	Type of food
rice	carbohydrate
cod	
margarine	
pork chop	
cream	
pasta	

7 Name two very rich sources of Vitamin C

8 Sally is slightly anaemic, she does not need iron tablets yet. What foods would she be advised to eat to get more iron into her diet?

9 Why is it not advisable to eat the right amount of energy from only beefburgers and chips?

10 Mohammed follows the Muslim religion, what restrictions does this place on his diet?

Planning meals

When you are planning meals for other people, the most obvious thing to do is to check their likes and dislikes before setting about it. There is no point in planning and preparing a meal that someone does not like. Enjoying your food is not possible if it is food you hate. Liver and kidney are both nutritious dishes mostly enjoyed by older people, lots of younger people will not attempt to eat it. Some foods have a bad effect on people, usually upsetting their digestion or "repeating" for a long time after a meal, cucumber and radishes often fall into this class. Some foods, like baked beans, cucumbers, radishes, onions, leeks and garlic give people painful wind so they avoid them. Actually healthy individuals should be able to take small amounts without too big a problem – it is all part of eating the wide variety of foods we talked about in a healthy diet. After finding their favourite dishes, remembering that you can please some of the people some of the time, it is time to think about the nutritional value, different textures, smells, colours and flavours of the food to make the meal interesting. Have you ever been served mashed potatoes, steamed cod fish and boiled cauliflower – think about it, they are all off-white in colour, all soft and the fish and cauliflower smells conflict. A meal like this would not look at all appetising to a sick client and it certainly would not stimulate the appetite with smell or appearance.

How could you make this more interesting?

Bake the potato or a few chips deep fired in healthy oil, add a parsely sauce or a sprig of parsely and slice of lemon to the fish and substitute peas for the cauliflower. The meal would look, smell and taste much better and you now have some different textures as well. So think about the meal in this way; when you are at home do not be afraid to experiment with different flavours and garnishes. A friend swears by mint sauce on simple baked beans on toast!

You also must consider when food is available, although with refrigerators and deep freezers many foods are now available all year

Figure 62   *Children may not always appreciate a healthy meal!*

round. Do not, for example, plan to serve fresh strawberries in December if you need to consider costs. They are available, flown in from hot countries but are awfully expensive; if you are trying to get Vitamin C into your meal, try adding a sauce made from tinned blackcurrants or adding a simple orange or apple to the meal. Most staple foods like bread, rice and pasta are available all year round and do not vary in cost between the seasons. Vegetables do vary, root vegetables like carrots and parsnips are available all through the winter months, but lettuce and tomatoes become more expensive then. A great deal will depend on the season in which you are planning the meal. You need to consider the age, culture and sex of your client for the meal. A healthy young man who is physically active will require a more 'hefty' meal than an older person or a child, with a good helping of staple food to fill them up. Someone from a different culture may assume that you know the foods they cannot eat and therefore may not tell you that they do not take pork for instance. Careful preparation is required. You also need to think about the setting in which you will prepare the meal.

What facilities are available for cooking? Can you grill, fry, steam, microwave, roast, bake and boil? If you have no microwave available then you need to think about the time your food might take to cook in more traditional ways. If you hope to gain merit or distinction for this unit, you will have a time deadline from your tutor in which to complete your assignment. You may have one anyway because other people need to use the facilities.

Find the time deadline from your tutor if you do not know this. It is an essential part of your planning to know how much time you will have. You need to divide the time up for preparation time and actual cooking time, leaving some minutes for arranging and serving food. Have you ever seen the TV programme 'Ready, Steady, Cook' where expert chefs have only half an hour to think up a dish and cook it from ingredients brought by guests. Try to watch, if you have not seen it before; you will notice that the chefs tend to cut food up into small pieces so that they will cook quickly; they also serve and present the food beautifully. Your tutor may also give you a budget limit for your meal, and at home or in work everyone has to work to budgets so

Figure 63   *Rushing to finish*

this is very sound practice. Take care not to spend most of your money on one item and have very little left for variety.

Preparing meals

If you are never involved with cooking at home and have never had a cookery or home economics class at school, then you will need to practise simple techniques.

BOILING, FRYING AND SIMMERING

Sometimes you need to start with the food in cold water and bring to the boil (when large bubbles burst at the top), other times you need to put the food in boiling water. You will need to check this either on the packaging instructions or in a cookery book together with the length of time the food should be boiled. Over-boiling often spoils the food, making it soggy or breaking it up. As soon as the food to be boiled is brought up to boiling point, then you can turn the heat down. You should have the occasional bubble bursting at the top. Take care with boiling water, it will scald if it splashes on your skin. Keeping food

just below boiling point while it cooks is known as simmering. Frying is usually done in a frying pan, but can also be done in a saucepan especially if you are going to add liquid and other ingredients later. Many foods which traditionally are fried like bacon can be done without adding much oil or fat as they contain a lot of fat in their structure. Certain good non-stick frying pans can be used to fry without oil or fat, so you need to check the equipment you will use. If you do need to add fat, then a little sunflower, corn or olive oil is best – do not swamp the food with oil! If necessary, you can add more later as the food absorbs the first oil. Try to fry fairly dry food so that it does not splutter and splash too much. Turning the heat down will also reduce the splashing or place a splashguard on the top. Frying is often messy, so do not forget to clean up after frying.

USING KNIVES

Experts always say that you are less likely to cut yourself if the knife is sharp than when it is blunt. Always cut on a board provided for the purpose and be extra careful when you get to the end of the food. Ensure that the flat surface of the food lies on the board; if the food is round like an onion take a slice off the bottom and place the cut flat surface downwards. If you can, hold the end of the food on a fork rather than with your fingers. Never pass a knife to anyone blade first and wash a knife with a brush, hot water and detergent. Do not leave a sharp knife in the bottom of a washing bowl with other utensils or you might pick it up sharp edge first. Dry knives from the back forward, not from the sharp edge back-wards and if you can, store them in a knife block. Always use the right size of knife for the job, do not cut a radish with a carving knife or a large piece of meat with a small vegetable knife.

USING MIXERS AND BLENDERS SAFELY

If you are unsure about the operation of the equipment – ASK. Use of machines like these should always be in accordance with the instructions of the manufacturer. Do not use a piece of electrical equipment if you think it is unsafe because of a loose plug or socket, trailing wires, burning smell or frayed flexes. Tell your tutor who will direct you to another piece of equipment. Anything loose and dangling can get caught up in a piece of machinery with rotating parts and that can be very dangerous. Make sure that long hair, jewellery and rings are tied back or removed when using mixers. Start a blender or mixer slowly and build up the speed to your requirements. Ensure that the machine is stopped and still before you remove any food form the bowl or attachment. It is sensible to switch off and unplug the machine as soon as you have finished, tidying away the flex. Blenders usually require firmly fitting lids to stop the contents from being flung out.

MIXING INGREDIENTS, FOLLOWING RECIPES AND INSTRUCTIONS ON FOOD PACKAGING

Recipes will provide you with the order for mixing the ingredients, and you will not get the best product if you alter the order and may, ruin the food altogether. Use the right type and size of spoon for adding ingredients and mixing them together. Follow the instructions on food packaging for preparing the food, be careful not to throw the packaging away too early!

GOOD HYGIENE IN FOOD PREPARATION

You have already learned about food hygiene in chapter 4, so it would be a good idea to revise the key principles outlined on pages 69–70 first. Here are a few points important in this unit:

- make sure that all surfaces and equipment are cleaned with hot water and detergent before you begin and also after you have finished, clean as you go is a good saying
- prepare yourself by tying back long hair and removing jewellery; wash your hands in hot soapy water before you begin and wear clean protective clothing; any cuts or abrasions should be covered over with blue adhesive dressings before you begin (this is to show them up if they fall off)
- always keep raw and cooked foods separate and clean utensils and equipment thoroughly before moving on to another food
- understand that bacteria causing serious food poisoning lurk on skin, hair, jewellery, surfaces and equipment and raw food.

Presenting food

You have learned that colour, flavour, texture and smell are important in planning and preparing a meal. Think about the way in which you will place food on the plate; don't put two similarly coloured foods next to one another, separate them by some other part of your dish. Place the sauce or gravy at the side of your plate in case the person does not care for too much of it. So make sure that nothing is dripping around the edge of the plate. If you can choose a dish or plate colour which adds to the arrangement. Put only a moderate portion size on the plate and vary the portion size to suit the client, smaller for children and older people than healthy adults. Remember to warm the plate or dish if you are preparing hot food; food goes cold very quickly if placed on a cold dish. Learn the correct way to place the cutlery if you don't know, making sure that it is shining and clean and adequate for the meal. A sparkling glass of cold water looks nice with a hot meal if you have not planned juice or milk with it.

Assessment evidence

You are asked to plan a balanced diet for a person for one day, the meals should provide the nutritional needs for that person. The person could be yourself, a friend, a member of your family or a client. Do not forget to say who the person is and describe their activities and nutritional needs in a short paragraph first. Identify the main nutrients in the meal and describe their functions. You might put this in the form of a chart for clarity. It might look something like this:

Meal	Nutrient	Purpose
Choice of breakfast	carbohydrate	supply energy
cereal, Weetabix or rice	fat	insulate against cold
crispies, with milk, hot	protein	growth and repair of cells
buttered toast and	Vitamins A,C and D	helps wounds to heal
orange juice		and prevents scurvy
	calcium	hardens bones and teeth

And so on…

You will work within a budget and prepare two courses from the daily menu you have planned. It would be an advantage if you could put the approximate cost against each item as you plan, then you can add up at the end and see whether you need to make alterations up or down. Another table would prove handy and you can include this in your evidence.

Menu	Approximate cost
Two Weetabix	20p
Half pint of semi-skimmed milk	18p

And so on…

Figure 64   *Well presented food*

If you are really good at making tables you can add the columns together and make one large table, probably better done with your paper longwise, called landscape mode. You can use a computer to produce this neatly as part of your portfolio evidence. A word of warning do not be too ambitious even if you are a competent cook. You will have limited time and money and are most likely to be working in unfamiliar surroundings. There are no extra credits for making curried chicken and rice than for making beans on toast! Consider carefully which course you will do, making two hot meals will be quite a feat, and you might be better off choosing breakfast and one hot meal or a sandwich supper and a hot meal. You could of course be really unimaginative and do breakfast and supper, in this case a hot breakfast might be more acceptable. Think carefully about the time that you will need to carry out all the jobs to

do with food safety like cleaning, it all takes time and most jobs take longer than we plan for. A time chart could be useful to you and it will also enable you to sort the tasks in the order that you want them done. While you are waiting for a food to cook, think about warming plates and presenting food arrangements, little tasks that could save you time at the end. Present your meals as you have planned to do. If you are trying to achieve a merit or distinction, then you will have some extra work to put in to your evidence.

FOR MERIT

- you will need to show that you can substitute some foods for others which supply the same nutrients, for example if you are considering a pork chop meal to supply protein, an omelette would be an alternative as eggs are also protein. You could refer to your plan of the day's meals and show which nutrients could be replaced by other foods as a short paragraph underneath – about four or five 'changed' foods should be enough.

● you will need to meet the time deadlines for your two courses in your assessment.

● prepare more than one food in a dish and make sure that it is not only hygienic but attractive to look at.

FOR DISTINCTION

You will need to:

● Evaluate your plan. In other words, describe what you did and why in terms of nutritional needs, time, resources and budget; to do this keep a log and a diary of all the changes you made stating the reason why.

● Present your courses in an attractive way which includes thought about the preferences of your chosen person – for instance if it was your mother and she loves flowers and her favourite colour is blue, you might include a bud vase on the place setting with a single blue freesia or small bunch of forget-me-knots. Look around your garden and it will not add to your budget.

● You will need to explain why you have done this and not ask anyone else.

Student activities

 1 When you have decided on your course, have a 'dummy' run at home

Figure 65   *An incorrectly laid table*

timing yourself at each stage' evaluate this in terms of your order of tasks. If you are seriously over the time limit, think about where you can save time. Carrying out the tasks a second time will let you see whether you can save time with more practice or not.

2 Draw simple flow charts of what you intend to do.

3 Try simple colour scheme arrangements for place settings using crayons or felt tip pens.

4 Ask your friends and family how they like their food arranged to give you more ideas.

5 Find out how to arrange food on a plate for a client who is visually impaired (cannot see very well or at all).

Self-check questions

☑ 1 Your chosen person has difficulty cutting with a knife; explain how you would overcome this difficulty.

2 Jawal is seriously over-weight, plan a meal which could be part of a weight-reducing diet.

3 Samantha is anaemic; plan a meal that is rich in iron for her.

4 Your father has just had an operation; advise your mother on the appropriate foods for his speedy recovery.

5 What is wrong in the diagram of a place setting on page 116?

ASSESSMENT EVIDENCE

You need to produce:

- a plan for a balanced diet that would meet the nutritional needs of a person for one day
- prepare at least two courses from meal(s) identified in the plan for the day
- work within a given budget to produce the two courses

To achieve a pass you must show you can:	To achieve a merit you must also show you can:	To achieve a distinction you must also show you can
• use commonly available food from the five food groups when planning the diet	• demonstrate a sound understanding of dietary needs by showing different ways of meeting them for your chosen person	• evaluate the diet plan based on nutritional content, time and resources, and available budget, explaining how it meets the needs of your chosen person
• plan the courses to meet the needs of the individual, identifying the main nutrients and their functions	• bring together the components of both courses within a realistic time frame, to meet deadlines	• demonstrate independent thought by presenting courses in a way that appeals to and suits your chosen individual
• prepare* the food hygienically and safely, meeting specific requirements of the food preparation area in which you are working	• combine foods appropriately in each dish and present the two courses in an attractive way	
• present meals hygienically and as planned		

*see teacher guidance with regard to students with special needs

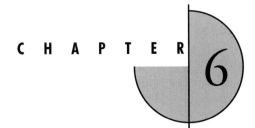

Exploring recreational activities for clients

CONTENTS AND LINKS

When you are looking after people it is important to recognise that they need to take part in recreational activities, just like you do, in order to have a well balanced and healthy lifestyle.

In this chapter, you will learn about:

- the benefits of recreational activity
- the recreational activities available in your community
- how these facilities can be used by clients to enhance their well-being

- barriers that might make if difficult for people to use health and recreation facilities
- health and safety factors associated with health and recreation facilities.

There are links with mandatory unit 2 (Understanding health and well-being), and possibly with Unit 9 (Working as part of a team).

Benefits of recreational activity

Recreational activities can be put into one of three main groups:

- *Physical* – where people are generally using muscular action to do the activity
- *Intellectual* – using your brain to work things out
- *Social* – where the main aim is to meet other people, and be able to talk to them and do things together.

Most recreational activities are actually a mixture of these, but with one aspect being there more than the others, for example, team games such as rugby, soccer or netball are physical as there is a lot of running around to do. They are also intellectual as you have to think about tactics, and social as you are mixing with other people all the time you are playing – and before and after the game. Swimming, however, is a physical activity done alone without much thinking necessary. Recreational activities do not have to be sporting, however. There are chess clubs, bridge and cribbage clubs that people go to, and dances, or rambling, birdwatching, fishing, debating societies or competitors clubs for people who enjoy entering competitions to win prizes.

Recreational activities for different client groups

Not everybody will want to do, or be able to do the same kinds of things for recreation. If you think about people in health and social care settings, they can be divided into client groups:

- children
- adolescents
- adults
- elderly people
- people with special needs.

Clients may be able to organise and take part in things with a small amount of help, but they may need a lot more doing for them. Apart from the day to day care staff of care assistants and nurses, they may need specialist help from physiotherapists, occupational therapists, play therapists or sports therapists and art therapists.

Student exercise

Part one

 Get hold of three pages of flipchart paper.

- With a marker pen, write on top of one page 'PHYSICAL', another page 'INTELLECTUAL', and the third page 'SOCIAL'.
- As a class exercise, think of as many recreational activities as you can, and write down each one on a stick-it note.
- Each person in the group should then take

turns in putting a stick-it note on the flipchart page under the heading where they think it fits best.

- The rest of the group can then discuss whether they agree of not that it is under the right heading, and move to if a majority think it should go under another heading.
- When every stick-it note is in the agreed place, each person should copy the lists for evidence in their own portfolio. Leave room on the right hand side of the page for the next part of the exercise.
- Do not forget to mention in your portfolio that the work was done as a class exercise.

Part two

- Using the three lists of activities you have copied for yourself to use, go through them all and decide which group each one would be most suitable for (use the list of client groups above for this).
- You could use colour coding (e.g. a black dot for children, a blue dot for adults and a red dot for special needs, etc.) or letters, A for Children, B for adolescents, C for adults and so on. Some activities will be OK for more than one group so it is alright to have more than one letter or colour by the activities.

We have to consider the suitability of a recreational activity. It is no good suggesting swimming for a female member of a religious group who is not permitted to expose any parts of her body except her face. So culture is one factor to consider. What could others be?

Age should be a factor, e.g. most elders cannot take part in strenuous physical games, but can enjoy keep fit exercises to music using large bean bags or balls. The exercise helps to keep joints mobile, stimulates blood circulation, promotes social activity and the 'feel-good factor'. Similarly, young children have not the strength to undertake vigorous activity for long periods of time, but can be 'on the go' with one physical activity after another for what seems like a long time.

Most adolescents, however, have the ability to undergo moderate physical exercise for some time e.g. game of tennis, squash or netball. Physical activity throughout childhood and adolescence helps bones form their final adult shape, stimulates blood circulation and hormone release and generally promotes bodily health. Walking, snooker, darts, gardening are all reasonable physical activities that many elders undertake.

All ages love parties, opportunities to meet friends and have fun together, and the same goes for trips or outings. As a result, people develop a common interest for discussion, reminiscence, have the opportunity to dress up and look special, while enjoying a change of scene. Discussions are particularly hard to keep going in a residential setting for elders, many cannot concentrate for long, some fall asleep, others have no interest in anyone else's views.

Adolescents on the other hand love to debate and argue both past and current issues, while children find it difficult to concentrate on talking about the same subject for too long. Families often hold discussions at mealtimes, but mealtimes as family occasions do seem to be declining, many adolescents prefer fast food with their friends, and often a parent is working antisocial hours.

Figure 66   *Swimming is a physical activity, rather than an intellectual or social one*

Fitness is another factor determining the suitability of recreational activities for people. Even unfit adolescents should not undertake strenuous physical exercise without some training beforehand. Several people each year get into serious life-threatening difficulties because they undertake dangerous activities without correct preparation, suitable equipment and training by professionals. Elders and children are less likely to get into trouble in this way, but families on a day out might become carried away with enthusiasm, because one member has some experience of the activity.

Gender is becoming less and less important in suitability of recreation. We now have plenty of female football and rugby teams, female wrestlers, snooker players and golfers. A few years ago, many of these would have been unheard of, but today there are many examples. Some males knit, crochet and sew, but on the whole these activities seem less acceptable to male client groups than females carrying out male recreational activities. With older people, it is probably less acceptable to suggest an activity perceived as the 'property' of the other gender, e.g. females undertaking a 'masculine' activity such as snooker. Younger people are not prone to such stereotyping.

The last important factor is budget. If you cannot afford the fees of the local country club, then there is no point applying to join. Do not aim to take up golf, if the only golf course around has a large joining fee and annual subscription, you have no wage and therefore limited finances.

Figure 67   *Females taking on an activity traditionally seen as a 'male' activity*

It has already been mentioned that it is foolish and often dangerous to attempt some activities without being correctly fitted out, e.g. rock climbing without suitable footwear. You will be able to think of many other examples; getting properly equipped takes money for hire or purchase.

Costs are a major barrier to many people taking up recreational activities which they would at least like to try. Hiring equipment is a cheaper short-term answer to purchasing but not in the long term. Club membership can be cheaper then paying on each occasion and discounts or concessions are often available for the unwaged, regular users, senior citizens or students, so it is well worth investigating the possibilities. There are often open days or opportunities to try unusual activities at festivals and shows. Still it has to be said that the costs involved do mean many people are seriously disadvantaged.

Student activity

- Examine your local newspaper (free ones are often the best for this) and collect cuttings about concessions, open days etc.
- If you live close to your local library, pay them a visit and find out if they keep a display of information about local recreational activities. You may be able to pick up some leaflets.
- Write to two or three clubs and ask if they have reduced costs or fees for certain client groups.
- Write a report about your findings for your portfolio.

Actually getting into a place where recreation is being carried out can be extremely difficult or impossible for some client groups. Even when getting in is not a problem other barriers may arise.

People with hearing difficulties may not be able to hear anything as they are so far away from the sounds. Stairs or absence of lifts may prevent people from getting to the right area. Corridors may not be wide enough for wheelchair users to move around safely. Fire regulations might interfere with the rights of wheelchair users to use the facilities, in case there is an obstruction when evacuating others.

Toilet facilities may be very limited particularly at shows and other outdoor events and totally impossible for wheelchair users. There may be age restrictions to some activities, children may not be allowed in, this bars families with young children, so the adults cannot participate either unless child care facilities are provided.

Finally, access to the activity may be provided but transport is the main problem. Cars, buses and trains are often inaccessible to people with mobility problems.

However, the news is not always gloomy, more and more people and organisations are adapting their premises to make them attractive and accessible to all. Transport providers are gradually changing some of their facilities and particularly, if they are given warning of disabled or elderly clients' travel plans, they can help a great deal. Leaflets are published to assist the disabled client.

There is no reason why people with special needs cannot take part in almost all activities, no matter how demanding they may seem. People who have legs and arms missing have climbed mountains; wheelchair users can abseil and dance; blind people can drive in properly controlled conditions (although not on public roads), and people who are paralysed can make parachute jumps with the right kind of help. There are wheelchair sports teams of all kinds, and drama groups and choirs for people with learning difficulties.

Although most recreational activities are done for enjoyment, there are sometimes other reasons why people are advised to take part.

These are 'therapeutic' reasons, which means that the activities are intended to help them improve their quality of life. When this is the case, then 'Therapists' will be involved to advise and guide on what to do, and how to do it safely. Some of those involved are:

PHYSIOTHERAPISTS

Physiotherapists are often called 'physios' for short. They work mostly in hospitals, but also for sports teams, and you can pay to go see them privately. Their main job is to keep the body moving, or get them to move better, e.g. after breaking bones or after a stroke. They may suggest recreational activities such as swimming or aerobics for people to do.

OCCUPATIONAL THERAPISTS

Occupational Therapists are called 'OT's' in the places that they work. They work mainly in hospitals and for Social Services. They look at how people manage in their day to day lives, and then make suggestions on how to improve things. This includes basic matters such as moving around the house, making meals, or keeping clean. Occupational therapy also includes ideas on how to get people mixing with other people, or doing things which will make them feel better in themselves. This might include going on shopping trips, going on outings or to clubs with other people, whether it is to play cards, go dancing or just to sit and chat. OT's may also encourage people to make things, such as pottery, carpentry or sewing.

PLAY THERAPISTS

Play Therapists use play to help children to learn and to develop skills, and to make them feel more secure. Some activities let children play at doing things that frighten them, so that they can practice for the real thing, such as going to a dentist or going into hospital. When a child is in hospital, a play therapist can give them things to do to stop them worrying about their illness.

ART THERAPISTS

Art Therapists encourage people to use art as a way to communicate and to express their feelings. It is very useful for people with mental health problems, and sometimes for people who have trouble reading and writing. This group may include people with learning difficulties, or who have had serious head injuries.

Art is not just painting things, but includes making thing as well, such as sculptures and models.

SPORTS THERAPISTS

Sports Therapists do not just treat sportsmen and women. They can advise on activities which can help to strengthen any physical weaknesses, and advise on rehabilitation programmes and mobilisation exercises. They often work with people with physical disabilities or mental health problems.

Regular exercise is known to increase self-confidence and reduce anxiety and depression. People often describe a 'feel-good factor' after taking part in exercise.

Student exercise

What you need to do now is to look at what recreational facilities there are in your local area. The first thing that you will have to do with your teacher or lecturer is to decide on what you are going to call 'local'. This will be different if you live in a town or in the country. The next thing to do is find out what facilities there are in the area you have chosen, and then going to look at what they have to offer. You may also want to invite somebody in to speak to the group, e.g. the manager of a Leisure Centre (see the exercise on Inviting a Speaker on page 11)

As a group, make a list of all the places for recreation you know in your chosen local area. Where are the swimming pools, parks, public football fields, pool halls, and library? Where are the pubs? What sort of different actitvities do they have there – are some more suitable to adults and some to adolescents? Are there disco's, quiz nights or 'Theme nights'? Are there places where people can go for walks, such as along the canal or on the river bank?

Do you know of any clubs, such as a Chess Club, or a Judo Club, Diving Club, Rock-Climbing, Caving, and so on? Ask at the library if they have a list of local clubs.

Once you have your complete list of leisure and recreational activities and local clubs, put down the headings of:

- Children
- Adolescents
- Adults

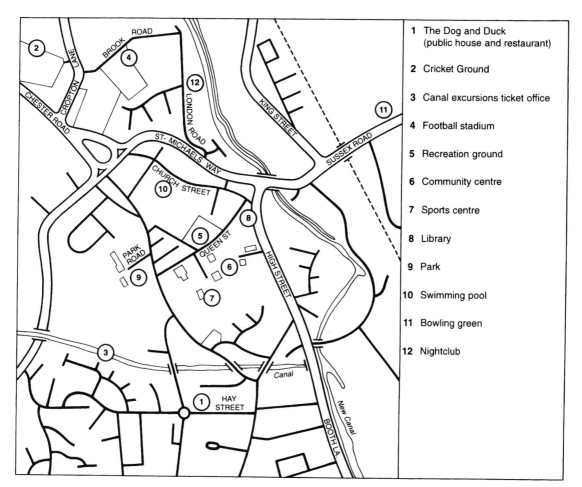

Figure 68   *A town map with key to show amenities*

- Elderly people
- People with Special Needs.

Under each of these headings, write the leisure and recreational facilities that you think would be most appropriate for each group. Some of the things will appear in more than one list; pubs might be fine for everyone, except children without adults; so might swimming.

Using the PIES information from Unit 3 (Understanding Personal development and relationships), decide which need is being met by each of these activities.

You can leave out the Emotional needs for this exercise.

Do the exercises on PIES again if you need to remind yourself about what they are. Get hold of, or draw a map of your area, and mark on it where all the places are that you identified as leisure and recreational facilities, giving them all numbers as a key.

When you have done this, make a guide to the places, giving information about each one: e.g.

1 Swimming Pool, Walton Street.
   Open every day from 10 a.m. to 9 p.m., except Sunday, when it is open from 10 a.m. to 6 p.m. Entry costs £1.20. They have sessions for women only, older people, and children. Also a disabled swimming club, and life-saving lessons.
2 Park and boating lake.
   The park is open every day from dawn until dusk.
   Boating lake boat hire from 11 a.m. to 7 p.m. daily from April to October.
   Rowing boats £1 for half an hour; pedal boats 50p for 15 minutes.
3 Leisure and Sports Centre, Dansdale Gardens.
   Squash courts, Indoor and Outdoor tennis, weight training, and sauna.
   Open from 7 a.m. until 11 p.m. every day.
   Has a Judo Club, Tumble Tots, Aerobics, Climbing Wall, and a Crèche.

Payment is for individual activities, or an annual fee of £450 allowing access to everything.

Continue with your list in a similar way to this, covering all the places you have found.

Barriers to recreational activities

One or two barriers to using these facilities have already been mentioned: not many places will let children in if they do not have an adult with them.

Some places have age restrictions, such as over 16s only; or over 25s. Crèches are for very young children, and you must have special needs to go to some of the clubs provided for people with special needs. One exception are the PHAB clubs (Physically Handicapped and Able Bodied). Anybody who wants to can go to them. To find out if there is one in your area, contact the library, or contact PHAB at Summit House, Wandle Road, Croydon CR0 1DF.

How easy are the places to get to? Are there buses that go there? How much is the fare from the town centre?

Other activities require you to very active and fit, such as the Climbing Wall, Scuba Diving and caving, parachuting or hang-gliding.

What is the access to these facilities like for people with a physical disability? Remember that if somewhere is accessible to a wheelchair, it will be accessible to other people with walking problems, or to parents pushing a pram or pushchair. Are there many steps, or revolving doors at the entrance, or once inside? Is the lift big enough for a wheelchair, and can someone sitting down reach the but-

Figure 69   *Hang-gliding*

tons? Are the buttons marked in Braille so that a blind person can use them?

The barrier to some activities is the expense. Some leisure clubs charge an annual membership of hundreds of pounds, and so do some golf clubs. Other activities require special equipment, such as sub-aqua diving, hang-gliding and parachuting, and motor racing. You may also have to travel a long way to get to them. There are not many motor-racing circuits in the country, and horse racing is only available in a few towns.

Some activities such as horse riding or judo require special clothing, which can be quite expensive.

When you have identifies the places people go for leisure and recreation, visit some of them and find out who the main users (or client groups) are. Are they mostly teenagers or older people? Are there particular times of day when mothers and young children are there, or sessions for older people?

Choose one of the places on your list, and a particular client group from the five given (children, adolescent, adults, elderly people, people with special needs), and ask the staff about how the group uses the facilities.

Some of the questions you might ask are:

- What is the benefit of the facility to your chosen client group?
- What are the barriers to participation?
- Is it very expensive?
- Is it difficult to get to?

Figure 70   *Can they reach the buttons?*

- Do the users need to bring any special equipment or clothing?
- Is it accessible to people with disabilities?
- Is it safe for unaccompanied children?

Write all your information up to put into your portfolio, explaining:
- Why you chose the recreational facility that you did, and why you did not choose any of the others.
- The benefits of the activity chosen for the group you have chosen
- Identify any barriers to access which you have identified (cost, too difficult to get to, only open in the day when the client group are doing other things, etc), and how they might be put right.

Key skills exercise

If you want to add evidence to your key skills portfolio, work out the costs for members of your chosen client group. This can include travelling costs, membership or entry fees (or both), and the cost of buying any special equipment.

HEALTH AND SAFETY FACTORS

Many of the recreational activities identified will have health and safety factors to take into account. Some activities are potentially quite dangerous, and planning to avoid as many hazards as possible is the sensible thing to do. Hazards are the possible dangers involved in an activity.

Here is some general guidance on health and safety for recreational activities:

- Do not let people overdo physical activity
- Be prepared for changes in the weather
- Always take expert advice on the activity you will be doing
- Know the rules and regulations for the activity
- Make sure that you have correct equipment, and that it is in good working order
- Have first aid equipment available, and someone who knows how to use it

Figure 71   *Judo*

- If anyone is on medication, take enough with you to cover a longer stay than you intend
- When travelling, make sure that everybody wears a seat belt when they are available
- If any special needs clients are involved, or young children do you have enough helpers to cope with them?
- When going on trips either walking or over water, let people know the route you intend to follow, and when you will be back
- Do you need to take out insurance? (Nobody can go parachuting, for instance, unless they have done this).

- For indoor activities, are there enough fire extinguishers about, are the exits clear?
- Are there enough lights, is the ventilation adequate?

There may be more questions you could add, and there will certainly be more when you know exactly what activity is to be done.

Let us take a look at a specific recreational activity; **swimming**, and identify some of the things that can go wrong. Looking at what can go wrong is sometimes known as a 'risk assessment'. Hazards linked with swimming in swimming pools are mainly drowning, and of people giving themselves head injuries or neck injuries if they dive in where the water is too shallow. There are also injuries caused by slipping on wet tiles. It is expected that people will be wearing appropriate clothing to go into the water. They should also wear buoyancy aids such as rubber rings or armbands if they need to.

Ways to avoid these hazards are to put up notices telling people not to run, not to dive in, and not to go into the deep water if they cannot swim. It also helps if at least one lifeguard is on duty to keep an eye on what people are doing, and either to stop them doing it or to rescue them and give first aid whenever that is needed.

Student exercise

 Now that you have an idea of what you have to do, write out your own risk assessment for **Rock climbing** and **Canoeing**. Remember to think of what can go wrong, and what can be done in advance to stop it going wrong.

ASSESSMENT EVIDENCE

You need to produce a report about locally available recreational activities and facilities. It must include:

- details of how the activities and facilities could benefit clients
- description of available activities for a client group
- identification of barriers to participation
- consideration of health and safety issues for the clients

To achieve a pass you must show you can:	To achieve a merit you must also show you can:	To achieve a distinction you must also show you can:
• correctly identify locally available facilities for recreational activities	• demonstrate a sound understanding of the benefits of different recreational activities	• analyse the use of the recreational activities by matching the specific needs of clients to the benefits
• clearly describe at a basic level how one client group benefits from these facilities	• realistically identify how potential barriers to access might be overcome for specific recreational facilities	• justify the selection of one particular facility for use by a client group, explaining why you rejected other facilities
• accurately identify basic health and safety issues related to the activities and the client group	• describe clearly how health and safety issues relating to recreational activities can be addressed	
• describe at a basic level common barriers to participation which might prevent the client group from making the best use of the facilities		

Understanding physical care

CONTENTS AND LINKS

This unit has links with all the mandatory units and some of the optional units such as Unit 8 (Preparing for employment in health and social care) and Unit 9 (Working as part of a team). It will help to prepare you for working in nursing or residential homes and give you an understanding about the work that you may do. You will learn how to work with clients to identify their needs and then to support them in meeting those needs. You will learn that providing support to clients must be done safely and in ways that help them to remain independent and keep their self-respect.

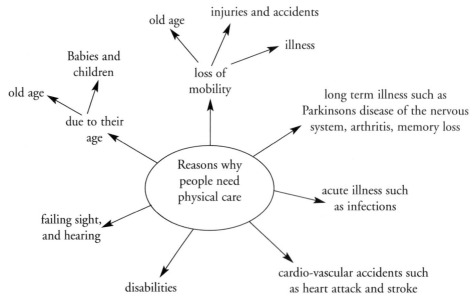

Figure 72   *Pattern diagram*

Why do people need physical care?

Everyone needs physical care during our life-times; and we needed it as babies or we would not have survived! You have probably had an illness or an injury at some point in your life, and if you haven't then you know someone who has.

The pattern diagram in Figure 72 shows you the various reasons why clients might need physical care.

CLIENTS WHO MIGHT REQUIRE PHYSICAL HELP

If you were asked to say who might need your physical assistance you would almost certain-ly mention elderly people. However, you must never assume because someone looks old they need help.

Many disabled and older people are fierce-ly independent and would be greatly offend-ed if you automatically went to give help. If the client is in residential accommodation this may mean they have a greater degree of dependence than a client living in their own home. But, remember, some clients are in res-idential accommodation for very different reasons. It is always wise to assume each client is physically capable of managing their own daily activities and alter what you do to suit each individual. It is also worth noting that setbacks in physical ability can be temporary and full independence can be regained after a short period e.g. broken bones.

When you start caring for people you are often so eager to help it is hard to curb your instincts. Most elderly people have lived in their own homes for many years before com-ing into care. They were used to making their own choices, meals, beds, entertainment, doing their hair, washing, shopping and so on. Most would have lived alone or perhaps with another similarly aged person. Think how you would feel suddenly moving into a home, with staff to look after you, and other people around most of the time.

Kindly staff probably pay a great deal of attention to a new resident when most of all they would like some peace and quiet to adapt to new surroundings and possibly mourn the passing of their old ways and inde-pendence.

Elderly people then, of course, must be mentioned if we are giving examples of clients who need physical assistance, but there are many others, in fact we certainly could not mention them all, and you will assist a lot of people who are not mentioned here!

Clients with restricted mobility means people who cannot move around as well as we can. Arthritis is a disease of joints which is very common. People suffer pain, swelling and stiffness which restricts movement. There are several types of arthritis, but there are two main types.

Osteoarthritis affects more people than any other form of arthritis. It is caused through wear and tear on the joints (usually the large joints such as hip and knee) so most-ly affects people in their later middle age and old age. Rheumatoid arthritis affects people at a younger age than osteoarthritis and more women than men. The joints are very painful, swollen and stiff and as the disease progresses many joints (usually the smaller joints at the wrist, hands and feet) become severely deformed.

Joints can be affected by other disorders such as haemophilia. This is a bleeding disorder, the blood cannot clot properly on its own. Children who have this disease usually inherit it from one of their parents and suffer bleeds into their joints and muscles as well as other places in the body. This causes painful deformity unless special treatment is given promptly.

Fractures of bones involving joints can lead to restricted movement and the onset of early osteoarthritis.

There is a group of diseases which affects the nerves which control muscles and therefore affects 'motor' skills. We use the term 'motor' to mean anything that brings about movement – in this case, muscles or nerves which control muscles. One such disease is called motor neurone disease (a neurone is a nerve cell) and can be inherited, affecting children or coming later in life, affecting mainly men over fifty.

Disorders of the brain can affect motor skills and the ability to receive sensations from the outside world. Some examples of clients with brain disorders who may need physical assistance are

- children and adults with learning difficulties and physical disabilities
- those who have suffered head injury, meningitis, abscess or tumour
- those who have developed degenerative disorders such as Alzheimers disease or Parkinsons disease.

Figure 73   *Never pre-judge someone because of their age – exercise classes can be useful for old or young people*

There are also cerebrovascular disorders or what we call strokes. The causes of strokes can be a clot forming in an artery (about 50% of all strokes), a bleed from a weak blood vessel (about 25% of all strokes) or a fragment of a clot from elsewhere in the body which is pumped round by the heart and gets stuck in a small blood vessel of the brain. This is called an embolism (about 25% of all strokes). It is usually extremely difficult to tell the exact cause when the damage occurs, which is why doctors and nurses tend to call these illnesses cerebrovascular (brain blood vessel) accidents, often called CVAs.

The extent of the damage and its effect on the client depend on how large the blocked blood vessel is, whether any blood can get to that part of the brain by any other route and where in the brain the blockage occurs. It is not so much that the blood vessel is blocked, but that part of the brain may not receive any oxygen from the blood and therefore die. If the part is large or is a very important area the person may lose consciousness and die. On the other hand, the client may barely notice the symptoms – about 33% of all strokes result in death, another 33% result in some

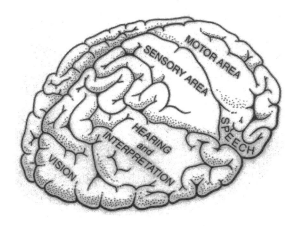

Figure 74   *Motor, sensory and speech areas of the brain*

disability, while the remaining 34% recover completely.

If the CVA involves the part of the brain known as the motor area, the client may have muscular weakness or paralysis on one side of the body. If it affects the most powerful side of the brain, (we all have one side more dominant than the other) speech may be lost or slurred, and if it affects an area behind the motor area, sensation may be lost, i.e. the part feels numb to the touch.

This numbness can be a form of sensory impairment. Blindness, partial sight, deafness (whole or partial) and loss of smell are also forms of sensory impairment.

All these clients may require physical assistance at some time of the day or night. The assistance you may need to give them in their daily routine might involve helping them cook food, feed themselves, get dressed or undressed or have a bath.

Some clients require physical help because their sight is defective or they are totally blind. This can occur from a fault before birth, during childhood and in adulthood due to eye disease or most commonly, as a gradually failure in old age. If you meet an elderly blind person, do not automatically assume they have recently had sight failure, even young blind people get old and they may be very skilled in ways to overcome the loss of vision.

You must be very careful not to *assume* anything or you will quickly fall into the habit of stereotyping. Assumptions are always based on prejudice! Hearing loss can occur at any time in a person's lifetime in the same ways as loss of vision. People may need help from you if they have a memory loss that can be temporary or permanent. Many old people can tell you wonderful stories from their early

Figure 75   *Some people need help to attend clinics*

childhood, but cannot remember where they put their glasses down. Memory loss can occur from head injury or strokes as well. A large number of middle-aged and elderly adults suffer heart attacks or become long term disabled through illness and they too may require your help.

Types of activity that may require help

Care workers often use the term daily living in care plans and in any one of these activities your assistance may be required.

Daily living activities might include:

- shopping
- preparing and eating food and drink
- washing, dressing and undressing

- using the lavatory
- housework
- gardening
- reading, writing, calculating, homework and hobbies
- answering telephones or doorbells
- moving about or going to see friends.

These are things most able-bodied people take for granted, but they are very difficult for some clients and may be impossible without your help.

Where is the help needed?

The answer can be – everywhere! However, most help will be needed in the clients own home or in care establishments such as day centres, nursing and residential homes, special schools and hospitals.

Who provides the care?

A large number of clients, including babies and most young children are cared for by members of their family. They might have a care professional visiting from time to time to check that everything is going well and there are no further requirements. For some elderly people living at home, friends will be a good source of help, particularly with outings, socialising, gardening and help with hobbies. When members of a family and friends help clients they are called informal carers and recently more government money has been made available through various agencies to give support and training, if required, to informal carers.

Then there are the professional careworkers or formal carers who are in paid care work. Some examples of these are:

- support workers
- social workers
- occupational therapists
- doctors
- hospital porters
- ambulance crews

- care assistants
- physiotherapists
- chiropodists
- nurses
- dentists
- and many more

Formal carers like these may work in a specialist care establishment like a hospital or travel around visiting clients' homes and residential care settings. They often gather with informal carers casually or in meetings to plan care. Finally, there are all the voluntary organisations who rely on interested people volunteering their time and skills to

Figure 76   *A good relationship is important*

help others. They may have a few paid workers as well. Here are some examples of voluntary organisations: Age concern, Help the Aged, MIND, SCOPE and The Children's Society. Voluntary organisations like these are always in need of helpers and money. They often have 'flag days' to raise money or have 'house to house' collections. Formal carers regularly contact voluntary organisations to help with their clients care, particularly when formal care is decreasing. Many organisations run day centres where clients can socialise and have baths etc. Voluntary organisations often lend special equipment out to clients perhaps to help with their daily living activities such as wheelchairs, zimmer frames and tip-up chairs.

Maintaining client independence and dignity

Several times through this chapter, we have made statements such as

- allow the client to do as much as possible for themselves
- let the client choose
- maintain the client's privacy

Let us now examine independence and dignity a little more.

If you make assumptions about clients then you are prejudiced. If you make assumptions about what other people want to do, say, wear, eat, sit, etc. you are imposing your will on them and taking away their identity, self-confidence, independence and choice. When you are there to give physical assistance, you are there to offer help only if it is required by the client. Listen to what a client has to say, observe their facial expression, body posture, gestures and movements to find out their wishes. Ask, communicate, use

gestures and body language yourself to give them as much choice as possible – and respect the answer.

Some carers will ask clients their wishes, but if the answer is not the expected one or convenient one, then ignore the response or pressurise the client to agree to an alternative. Negotiation can take place, that is part of everyday life, but the client should be able to compromise or not, for themselves. Clients should be offered respect, even though they may be difficult at times. We all have our good and bad days, our moods and degrees of cooperation. The pleasant client has a right to be different if something has upset them.

Many clients might find it difficult to join in certain social activities, but the carer must not decline to invite that client or turn down an invitation on their behalf without asking first. Clients with disabilities must not be labelled 'the rheumatoid arthritis in the second bed on the left', 'grumpy' has eaten his breakfast this morning and so on. In fact, clients should be given their correct name and title unless permission has been given to call clients by their first names. Carers must recognise that they cannot solve all their clients' problems, in fact they probably solve very few, but more often support clients in ways which help them work through their difficulties and suggest solutions for themselves.

Carers, then, must accept clients for being the way they are, at any particular time on any particular day. They must not judge the way they are, not compare them or expect them to be like other clients. If we are to develop good caring skills to support clients we must show

warmth,
understanding
and sincerity.

This is done by being sensitive to clients' needs, treating them as whole human beings, using communication skills to convey acceptance, allowing them to retain and develop their personalities, giving personal choice whenever possible and trying to put ourselves in their shoes, to share their feelings and experiences as much as possible.

Clients should be involved in as much of their care as is practicable and results of medical examinations, outpatient visits and similar events should be discussed with them in private. If a client discusses something in private with you, it should be treated as confidential and not discussed with anyone else or recorded in notes. Confidentiality is the right of every client whether the information is written, verbal or recorded on computer. If the information puts either the client or some other person in danger, then you have the right to say to the client that you must inform your line manager. You have reached the limit of your confidentiality.

When do clients need physical assistance?

Observation of movement is important, if a client is clearly trying to carry out a task and movements are repeated several times unsuccessfully, than a tactful offer of help can be made. Do not be offended if the offer is turned down. You should be please that the client shows determination, perseverance and the independent spirit you are trying to encourage.

A client who is tense and anxious can show this by clenching fists, white knuckles, clenched jaw, hunched shoulders. Someone who does not want to talk to you can be partly turned away bodily or facially and have their arms or legs folded. They may wave you away with their hands or shake their heads if they do not wish you to carry on. A client sitting with head down or held in their hands is often depressed, sad, in pain or feeling hopeless.

The face is often said to mirror the emotions, very few of us can be distressed and not let it show on our face.

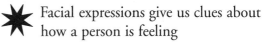 Facial expressions give us clues about how a person is feeling

- frown – puzzlement, anger
- eyebrows raised – surprise, horror, questioning
- mouth with corners turned down – disapproval, depression, sarcasm, disbelieving
- mouth with corners turned up – joy, contentment
- lip biting – nervousness, worry

You will be able to think of many more.

If you need to ask a client questions to find our their wishes, try to ask open questions which begin with how..., when..., where... etc. and allow the client to answer as fully as they wish. Using open questions will enable you to collect a lot of information without repeating questions. Closed questions usually can be answered with one-word answers. To open the question, instead of asking 'what is your name?' you could say to a new client, 'what would you like to be called?' That should produce more opportunity for discussion. You might receive the response such as 'my name is Florence Wrighton, most people call me Mrs Wrighton but, as this will be my home from now on, I would be happy to be called Flo'.

If you are working in a residential or nursing home, you will get to know the clients and their needs. For instance, you would know after you have been there a short while that Cyril always needs someone to help him use the lavatory and wash his hands. In that case, quietly follow him to help; don't shout out 'Going to the loo, Cyril?' that would cause him to lose dignity and might make him feel embarrassed and annoyed. It is also an invasion of his privacy; you might come to a private arrangement that he gives you a nod of his head when he needs your assistance.

What to do when helping clients with physical care

DRESSING

When helping clients to dress or undress, a little bit of planning may save a lot of time later. If the client is able to say which clothes they prefer to wear then you are unlikely to have any difficulty getting the clothes accepted. If some items of clothing are unsuitable for the season try adding layers in winter or omitting under layers in summer but let the client choose. Remember, you may not experience the weather in the same way as an older or more restricted person. Activity generates heat to keep us warm and younger people tend to have more fat under the skin than an older person, which alters the amount of body heat we gain or lose.

Not only do we put on clothing for privacy, well-being, warmth and protection, but we use our clothing to express our personal identity. Once again, being observant and knowing your client helps you tremendously as you are likely to indicate the types of garments your client likes to wear. Remember to take account of cultural and religious modes of dress as well as whether the client can cope

with the fastenings on the clothing, the size and the style.

Lay the clothes out in order in which they need to be put on together with any aids which will help the client to do it on their own. Confused or elderly clients often mistake the order in which clothes should be put on.

There are many ways in which dressing can be made easier for clients who are elderly or restricted in their movements. Buttons can be replaced by touch and close tape, devices on a stick to hold stockings and tights open so that the client does not have to bend. Some ladies might prefer trousers or warm track suits and socks doing away with the need for stockings etc., others would never dream of wearing such garments.

Shoes are worthy of special mention. Elderly clients should be encouraged to wear proper shoes, rather than slippers or soft moccasins, for a time each day. Feet not used to shoes flop about and quickly get unused to support, which then causes pain when shoes are worn, so setting up a vicious circle. Many people may need specially fitting for shoes or shoes may need to be adapted, e.g. with touch and close fastenings.

When helping people with restricted movement in one limb to dress, place that limb into the clothing first as the other can bend and thus be more flexible to place in the other half. When undressing, remove the good limb first and slide the clothing off the affected side. Think how you would do it to minimise your own pain if you had an injured arm or leg.

...AND EQUIPMENT

There are aids to help people dress themselves, keep independent and maintain dignity. Long-handled tools reduce the need for bending and lifting arms. Combs, shoe horns, bath sponges, gripping devices are all available on extended handles. A useful device for pulling clothes over shoulders is a long stick with a simple hook on the end. Button fasteners are available but many people replace buttons and zips with touch and close tape, much easier for arthritic people and elderly people to manage. Elastic shoe laces give the appearance of neatly fastened shoes while enjoying the simplicity of slip on shoes.

Socks, stockings and tights are all difficult to manage for people with reduced motor skills. Tights are particularly awkward because two legs have to be controlled at the same time! Simple but very effective devices are around to help with these, the socks are put on to the flexible plastic 'arms' and lowered on long handles to the feet, the foot is placed inside the arms and the sock is slowly pulled upwards over the feet by the arms.

WASHING AND BATHING

Not everyone can be bathed at the same time of day in residential accommodation, so bathing often makes people appear difficult or resentful if the time given does not suit them. Take a little time and trouble to help clients find an acceptable time, but even then slavishly following a timetable should be avoided, if an individual does not feel like a bath, it should not be forced. Bathing should be a calming, relaxing experience, the client should be encouraged to do as much as possible for themselves to maintain their own privacy and dignity. Everything should be ready at the beginning of the bath as on-one likes waiting while wet for something to be found and it can be highly dangerous to leave a dependent client on their own while something forgotten is fetched.

Bathroom safety precautions should be observed such as non-slip mats, safety rails, dry, clean floors and no electrical equipment etc.

With everything ready and the bathroom door closed, help the client to undress making sure their clothes they will wear after the bath are ready. Check the temperature and depth of both water with the client and double check these are correct before the client enters the bath. Use the toiletries the client wishes and ensure that the client's body is washed all over. Most people appreciate their back being washed. Allow plenty of time, both for the bath and dressing, allowing the client to do as much as possible. While the client is busy, you can be busy tidying and cleaning the bathroom while chatting to them Many problems come to light in the intimate warmth of a bathroom, but take care with confidential information.

Warm towels and help with drying are usually appreciated, but too vigorous rubbing should be avoided if the skin is thin and wrinkled. Pay particular attention to crevices where the skin folds. Such areas are under the breasts, between the thighs and toes. Cutting nails is much easier after a bath as they are softer, but many clients might require the expert help of a chiropodist.

Some clients prefer showers, others hate them – people should be allowed free choice. Showers are safer for clients provided that there is good temperature control, use of non-slip mats and provision made for drying the floor after each shower. It is more difficult for helpers to assist clients with washing in the small confines of a shower cubicle, unless they wear swimsuits.

There are many aids to assist with bathing and many specially adapted baths, but, here we have just been concerned with the actual process.

...AND EQUIPMENT

Costing several hundreds of pounds are powered bath lifts, and lever-operated bath lifts which raise and lower the seated client in the bath. Slightly less expensive is a turning bath seat – the client sits on the seat from the side of the bath and turns swinging the legs over the bath side. Simple seats which hang on the bath side are relatively inexpensive. (Remember baths are often slippery places, so anti-slip mats inside and outside the baths are a must for clients with restricted movement.) Grab rails and holding rails are important aids around baths, hand-basins and toilets where clients need something to hold on to while carrying out their personal hygiene. Seats in showers are useful, particularly for frail elderly clients.

COOKING AND FEEDING

Equipment for use in the kitchen might include kitchen tools with a good grip, extra large handles made of soft grip non-slip rubber, such as potato peelers, can openers, scissors. There are special holding tools because it is very difficult to grate cheese, butter bread, cut vegetables and carry out many other kitchen tasks if you only use one hand. Try it yourself next time you are in the kitchen preparing food.

Knives can be obtained with specially angled blades and easy to hold handles. They are for people who have very little strength in their hands and wrists.

Tipping equipment for kettles and teapots also help clients use them more easily and safely. Taps can be very difficult to turn if you have arthritis or weak wrists and long levers attached to taps make life much easier.

USING THE LAVATORY

Taking a small child to the lavatory is not a particularly hard task and you have probably done this many times. They may need help with difficult clothing and bottom cleaning after passing a motion. Always teach a child, particularly small girls to wipe from the front to the back and **not** the other way round. In females, the openings into the body from the front to the back are the urethra (for the exit of urine), the vagina (part of the reproductive process) and the rectum/anus (for the exit of motions). The urethra (and vagina) is liable to receive a large supply of infection-causing bacteria from the motions if the bottom is cleaned from back to front. This can cause very painful bladder infections (cystitis) and dangerous kidney infections. This applies to all females, not just youngsters. Moist toilet tissues are more comfortable for wiping than dry toilet paper and both the young and the elderly appreciate the softness. They can be purchased nowadays at most supermarkets, but are more expensive than toilet rolls.

Hand washing is essential for all after toilet visits to prevent bacterial contamination. Make sure that the toilet and washbasin are left in a clean and hygienic state after the visit. Elderly people have more difficulties using the lavatory because they might have:

- difficulty removing their clothing
- mobility problems such as getting out of the bed or a chair, getting to the lavatory and turning round
- pain
- arthritis in their hip joints, that means stiffness on bending

- confusion or memory loss – finding the lavatory in time can be a problem
- disorders of urination – incontinence, infection, males – enlarged prostate glands, bedwetting.

Incontinence can be either of urine or motions (faeces) and means that the client has lost control. They may pass urine or faeces without warning. An incontinent client in a residential or nursing home will usually be following a special plan aimed at getting the continence back, so you need to make sure that you know how the incontinence is being managed. Infection and enlarged prostates in males cause urgency (when urine starts to flow almost immediately after feeling the need to go) and frequency (going repeatedly after very short intervals) so you will need to show a lot of understanding with these clients. They get very worried about visiting the lavatory as they have probably had 'accidents' in the past and this makes urgency and frequency even worse.

Taking someone to the toilet before a meal is a good idea, but never force them to go. Their meal is not as likely to be disturbed, the hands get washed as well and they will be more comfortable to take food. Encouragement may be needed, a ready smile and a helpful suggestion tactfully made will work wonders with most clients. Make sure that the client uses hand-rails if at all unsteady and is stopped from sitting down until ready. This is the dangerous part, if a client falls off a toilet there are usually lots of things to bang heads on, little space to move to lift him or her even with help and the possibility of serious injury. When close enough to the toilet, let them turn slowly round and take short steps backwards until the edge of the sear is felt close to the knees. Instructing them all

the way is reassuring or annoying, you will have to judge your client's competence for yourself. Next, the client leans slightly forwards and very slowly lowers themselves on to the seat of the toilet. Slow, controlled movements are the keys to successful toileting. Rising from the toilet should be done with feet as far back as possible with bent knees, leaning forwards and pushing up using handrails.

... AND EQUIPMENT

For young children, easily cleaned steps and an inner lavatory seat should be available, this will give them confidence and they will soon start to do it for themselves. Some children are able to move straight from nappies to the toilet and leave the awful potty stage out altogether.

Older people should not have to move far to the sign-posted lavatories and washbasin. There should be plenty of appropriately placed handrails and for wheelchair users guard frames around the lavatories themselves. Removable high toilet seats are available for those who find standard seats too low. Places to put zimmer frames and walking sticks are useful as sticks fall about and can be a nuisance.

MOVING AROUND

There is an old saying in care – '**use it or lose it**' – and it is so very true. If you have ever had to stay in bed for a week or longer because of ill health, you might have noticed how your legs felt wobbly. This was because the leg muscles had become weaker as they had not been bearing your weight for a week. Every time that you give an old person who doesn't need help your arm to steady them or help them to stand, they have moved one step

Figure 77   *Child using a toilet step and seat insert*

nearer to using mobility aids including wheel-chairs. This is a dreadful thought, **a person who cannot walk loses vital independence**. This is an example of being cruel (not really) to be kind. Inaction leads to less action, so if you know a person can do it by themselves even with a struggle, let them do it. It can often be hard to watch a person struggling but imagine that wheelchair looming and you can do it. Often, providing a suitable aid will lessen that struggle, but keep the person mobile and it should be provided rather than resort to staff assistance every time.

...AND EQUIPMENT

Aids for mobility

These are aids to help people unable to get around using their legs or can only do so for short periods of time or with great difficulty. The simplest aid with which we are all familiar is the walking stick. The best varieties, a little more expensive than those bought in an ordinary shop have large handles to fit the hand. Some types have wide specially shaped handles to allow the weight of the hand to be

spread evenly over the handle. Others come in designs capable of being folded.

Giving yet more support are walking frames. Various types exist, some with wheels and some can be folded to fit neatly into a car. Walking frames can have bags attached so that shopping, books, knitting and money can be carried.

Some frames can be awkward to direct around corners or take outside, three- or four-wheeled walkers fitted with brakes are, however, very flexible. Some types have seats attached so that when the journey is tiring, the client can rest for a while.

The aids mentioned so far have been for people with some mobility, for those with very little, there is the familiar wheelchair. Most have large rear and small front wheels and fitted brakes. People undertaking sport-ing events have specially adapted lightweight, easily manoeuvrable wheelchairs. Most wheelchairs are capable of being folded and have comfortable padded seats. To use a wheelchair to climb to a higher level, ramps are necessary and portable ramps are available. Wheelchairs cost several hundred

Figure 78   *Aids for motor skills*

pounds. The ultimate aid is of course a specially adapted car costing several thousand pounds.

SITTING COMFORTABLY

High back chairs with extra support suit most elderly people; cushions can be used to support weak or paralysed arms. Chairs for sitting at the table are better with arms and with cushioned seats. Elderly people spend much of their waking time in a chair, so it must give the right support. The same sort of instructions for sitting down as for the lavatory is appropriate.

... AND EQUIPMENT

Seats can be adjusted for people who require high or low seats, and some chairs have slightly tipping sprung seats to assist the standing up process.

BEDTIME COMFORT

Firm mattresses on beds higher than the standard are preferred for elderly people, but the beds must not be too hard as you want as much of the body surface to be in contact with the bed as possible. It is a well-known fact that people living in a residential home

Figure 79   *Use of a high backed chair*

and pressure sore free can rapidly develop sores after an admission into hospital; this is often blamed on the hard beds and the bedclothes. Flannelette sheets are cosy in the winter months and coloured sheets look more welcoming.

Clients should have their choice of the number and type of pillows – it is their home after all.

A common mistake made by clients when getting into bed is to sit on the edge of the bed close to the pillows, then when they swing their legs up they are too high in the bed and have to strain to achieve the right position for lying down. Sitting halfway down the bed solves the problem. When getting out of bed, the client should sit up in

bed for a few minutes then swing the feet and legs to the floor, waiting again before leaning forward and rising. Many elderly clients have low blood pressure and if they suddenly get up from bed, the brain has not had time to adjust the blood pressure and they feel faint and giddy. Blood pressure needs to rise when standing as it has to force blood higher to the head and neck. Lack of blood circulating to the head causes fainting; this is why the first aid treatment for fainting is to lower the person's head to a position that is lower than the heart.

... AND EQUIPMENT

Ripple and water mattresses are used to prevent pressure sores, but they must be used correctly according to the manufacturer's instructions and adjusted to suit the client. Inverted V-shaped cushions are very useful for clients who need to half sit or half lie in bed because of heart or lung disease. Bed rests (like a small cut-off upholstered chair) can be used for a client who might be temporarily confined to bed with a heavy cold or short illness.

Seeing and hearing

SEEING

Clients should have their sight tested regularly, there are eye conditions that appear slowly without a person noticing. Most clients will wear spectacles at some time and the prescriptions for these must be kept up to date.

Books in large print or braille will enable a client with visual impairment to enjoy reading. Talking books are also important substitutes for reading. Magnifying glasses may assist a client to sew, knit or carry out similar leisure pursuits. Large print playing cards allow a client to participate in card games.

A guide dog is a living aid, allowing a client with severe visual loss, increased mobility and companionship.

Clients with less severe visual loss should have spectacles produced to their own prescription by an ophthalmic optician. Large thick felt pens and a pad may help in communicating with some people with poor eyesight.

HEARING

As with visual aids, hearing aids must be well maintained, often a client will switch off the aid, so do check that it is working.

The most common aid is the hearing aid and most of us are familiar with clients who use them. Other aids are available.

- Headphones. Special devices for listening to television.
- Induction loops. Wire loops set up around the room or building and people using hearing aids can pick up the electronic signals without also hearing background noise. Churches, cinemas and public halls often have induction loops.

Relevant health and safety issues

USING WHEELCHAIRS

This is best demonstrated for you will remember what you have seen better than reading a book. You can then try for yourself and be corrected. Some important points for you to remember are listed below:

- let the clients wheel themselves if they are able to do so
- never wheel a client to save time if they can walk (are ambulant)
- make sure that footrests and armrests are in position before moving
- use the brake whenever you or the client stops.

If you are involved in transferring clients to and from wheelchairs then:

- let the clients manage the transfer themselves if they can
- plan exactly what you are going to do and make sure that everybody involved is aware of the plan
- explain to the client what you are going to do and his/her part in the move

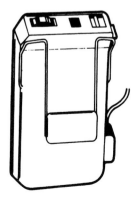
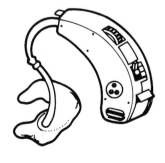

Figure 80   *Hearing aids*

- make enough space to carry out the transfer
- always position the chair as close to the next location as possible
- make sure that the footrests and at least one of the armrests is down before the move and that the brake is on
- point your feet in the direction of movement and have legs apart for a firm stand
- always keep bent knees and straight backs. (this does not mean straight up, the back is usually at an angle) not curved or rounded
- place your arms under the clients' arms and around the back so they feel secure
- straighten your legs to lift the client, do not use your back and vice versa when lowering the client
- do not change from the plan in mid-lift, if you are in trouble replace the client and re-plan carefully
- remember that for some clients movement is painful, they may scream out, be prepared for this.

Do not lift manually if you can avoid it.

Student activities

1 In pairs, make lists of your own daily living activities

2 If you work either voluntarily or as an employee in a care establishment choose two clients who need physical help from you or another assistant. Write two short accounts of why each client needs help and what physical help each client needs to carry out everyday activities such as cooking, feeding, dressing and bathing.

- If you do not have the opportunity to find this information direct, then ask a care assistant to talk to you about the sort of help some clients need. However, in both cases remember confidentiality and avoid real names and anything else which might identify the clients.

3 In pairs, with one person in turn blindfolded, practise eating your lunch or tea with the least physical assistance. Imagine the difficulty if you were walking into a dining room you had never been able to see. How would you assist someone to get through the doorway in single file, find a table, eat a meal and go to the toilet afterwards?

4 Describe what you know to be the important rules when lifting an object and a client.

- Observe and record a care assistant carrying out a lift. Make your own informal assessment.

5 In pairs, role play a new client and a care assistant and then exchange roles to be a new care assistant with a long-term client in residential accommodation. Using open questions, practise obtaining as much information about the likes and dislikes of the client in eight minutes.

6 Trying to use the sources of information in activity 2 in this chapter, explain how you or the carer would recognise when each client needed assistance.

- How would you give that help while maintaining each client's independence and dignity.

7 Mr Edward Jones is 83 years of age and has recently suffered from a stroke. This left him with a right arm and leg which are much weaker than normal. He now has difficulty in dressing, feeding and walking. For the past five years, he has been progressively becoming deaf in both ears, he has done nothing about this, putting it down to old age.

- Describe Mr Jones' needs.
- Choose one manual and one automatic aid and describe how each physical care aid you have chosen meets Mr Jones' needs, how each aid should be used in the correct

health and safety manner and what constraints (restrictions) there could be in the use of each aid for Mr Jones and for the other clients.

8 Practise using a wheelchair with a friend exchanging places after a while. Describe what it felt like.

9 Wear glasses covered with two layers of plastic film to affect clearness of vision (pieces from a plastic pocket will work well) and sit with your friends during a break. What did it feel like to be seriously visually impaired in a group of 'seeing' friends?

10 Try eating jelly with a blindfold or the glasses in Activity 9.

11 Tie your preferred arm to your side for about two hours and experience what it is like for a client with a paralysed arm from a stroke.

12 Find a voluntary organisation in your area and ask permission to visit; offer some help by being a collector of donations.

13 Ask care professionals to come and talk to your group about the physical care they give to clients.

14 Find either a catalogue of physical care aids to study or visit a centre for physical aids.

Assessment evidence

You are required to demonstrate an understanding of the physical care needs of a person receiving care and identify the difficulties that s/he may have in carrying out the activities of daily living. You may be able to do this by using a case study (anonymous to respect confidentiality) of a person you have met if you visit a voluntary organisation, nursing or residential home. You may also have a family member such as a grandparent who receives care. If you are in difficulties, ask a parent or guardian if they know of an elderly neighbour or friend whom you could visit.

You will have to think about the questions you need to ask beforehand and check them over with your tutor. You must not give offence by launching into your task by asking if they are incontinent for example. You may need to visit several times, find out if you can be useful when you visit – weed a patch of garden or dust some shelves they cannot reach. Use tact and respect their dignity at all times.

Having found your person, they are out there, you only have to look, list and describe the physical care support needed by the client and how any aids to daily living activities work. They may not have them, but they could be appropriate to your client. Finally, you need to demonstrate safe practice in giving the practical support for your individual. You might not be able to help with feeding and dressing without giving offence, but you could use a friend for simulation (pretending) and be assessed on that. If you work or have a placement in care, than that would be an ideal time to demonstrate your skills. Organise this with your tutor.

If you have done all this with a degree of competence than you will achieve a pass grade.

TO ACHIEVE A MERIT

In addition to the pass grade work, you need to explain how the physical care needs may be met while maintaining the dignity, self-respect and independence of your chosen person. You will do this by offering choices, maintaining privacy and generally treating the person as an individual. Is s/he is not a grandparent, imagine that they are – how would you like your grandparent to be treated in a care setting?

Then, you need to make a clear description of the possible risks to either yourself or the client in relation to the support you are giving. If you are feeding a partner to simulate feeding support, you will need to describe the risks to your client (in this case, there will not be many to you except possible scalding as you are not eating the food).

TO ACHIEVE A DISTINCTION

You must show that you have a good grasp of the balance between giving the best level of support and yet maintaining the need for their independence. You may need to let the person with poor vision cope with their own meal. You would tell them what the meal consisted of and using the positions of the hands of a clock, say the mince is at 12 o'clock, the mashed potatoes are at 6 o'clock, carrots are at 9 o clock and cabbage at 3 o clock. You might also say 'I would eat that meal with a spoon and fork' but allow them to choose whether they used a knife and fork or spoon and fork. Try to find at least three examples.

Finally, you need to make realistic suggestions as to how the risks to health and safety could be avoided. For an example, the only confused client in Silverfarm residential home was a fairly new resident Cyril Jones, and he had accidents because he never got to the toilet on time. You noticed that he went a lot of times to the toilet during the course of the day and had urgency as well as frequency. Staff were worried about George who was severely visually impaired, but fiercely independent, slipping on the wet floor if he followed Cyril into the toilet after one of his 'accidents'. The staff decided that one of them should always accompany Cyril to the lavatory. Cyril was annoyed at this and refused to tell the staff where he was going. The staff, already very busy, then had to follow Cyril whenever he left the day room. You suggest that Cyril see the doctor in case he required antibiotics to cure an infection or treatment for an enlarged prostate gland. In the meantime, Cyril could be provided with the material for cleaning up urine accidents and the toilets should be clearly signed which they were not.

ASSESSMENT EVIDENCE

You need to produce an investigation into the physical care of a person in a caring situation. It must include:

- the physical needs and support required
- demonstration of practical caring skills whilst observing safe practice

To achieve a pass you must show you can:	To achieve a merit you must also show you can:	To achieve a distinction you must also show you can:
• demonstrate a basic understanding of the physical care needs of the person by identifying the difficulties that may be experienced with daily living activities • list and describe the appropriate physical care support needed by the client and how any aids to daily living would operate • safely demonstrate the provision of practical support for the individual	• explain how physical care needs may be met so as to maintain the client's dignity and independence • describe clearly the potential risks to health and safety in relation to the support you have identified	• decide how to balance the best level of support for the person with the person's need for independence • make realistic suggestions as to how the health and safety risks could be addressed

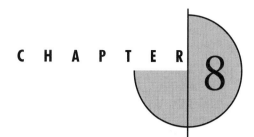

CHAPTER 8

Preparing for employment in Health and Social Care

CONTENTS AND LINKS

This unit is to give some advice, guidance and practice on how to find a job or training in health and social care. You will find out about the different ways of looking for jobs or training, and which ones are going to be suitable for you. You will be given practice in how to apply for jobs or training courses, and the various ways used to decide whether or not you are suitable for them. It will help you to work out your strength, skills and interests and to match them to the job or training that would best suit you. You will also find out how to prepare for a job or training interview, and given the chance to practise for these.

WHERE TO LOOK FOR JOBS AND TRAINING OPPORTUNITIES

Finding jobs

When you have finished your GNVQ and are looking for a job, what do you have to do?

Firstly you need to decide what type of job you are interested in. You may change your mind as you find out more about what you are expected to do when you are working in that job. This is fine, we are all allowed to change our minds if we want to. One decision you may want to make is whether to go for a paid job or for a voluntary job. If you cannot get a paid job, it is sometimes worth considering a voluntary job so that you can get experience, and this will help you to get a paid job later. We will start with voluntary jobs.

Voluntary jobs

There are opportunities for doing these locally, nationally and abroad. That is, near where you live, other places in this country, or in other countries.

Locally, you should look in the local newspaper and in the telephone book to see if there is a Council of Voluntary Service (CVS) or similar organisation. They are the place that many small voluntary groups use to recruit volunteers. They may want volunteers to help do the shopping for housebound people, or babysitting and granny-sitting services to allow the informal careers to get out now and again. Another job might be to help the voluntary organisations to get money, so collecting on flag days or working in a Charity shop could be something you might like to help with. Look at the notice boards in your school or college, there may be posters or letters asking for voluntary help.

A good organisation to get in touch with if you want to move about and get some really interesting experience is CSV, or Community Service Volunteers. They are at 237 Pentonville Rd., London N1 9NJ Telephone 020 7278 6601.

The Volunteer Centre UK will also give information about volunteering. They are at 29 Lower Kings Rd., Berkhampstead, Herts HP24 2AB, telephone 01442 773311.

For more adventurous people, there are places that will help you work in other countries. Bunacamp and CampAmerica take people to work with children every year at American summer camps. Look for their advertisements in newspapers and magazines.

Voluntary Services Overseas (VSO) are often looking for people to work all over the world, although usually they want people with qualifications to do specialist jobs. You can contact them at: VSO, 317 Putney Bridge Rd., London SW15 telephone 020 8780 7200

Paid jobs

When you are ready to look for a paid job, there are still decisions to be made. What type of work are you interested in? Even in health and social care there are lots of different types of work to do. As you have learned whilst doing this GNVQ, there is either direct work in looking after people, or indirect work

looking after the buildings and the equipment and services needed by the direct workers.

If you are interested in direct work, what sort of people would you like to be helping? Do you prefer looking after older people or children? Mentally ill people, those with learning difficulties or people with a physical

Figure 81   *Advertising can be effective*

disability? There are other groups, but these are the main ones. Next you will have to decide whether you are able to do work part time or full time, and whether you could work shifts or nights or prefer just 9 till 5.

Where to look

So where can you find out about what jobs are available?

NEWSPAPERS AND MAGAZINES

One of the easiest things to do is get hold of a local newspaper. If you do not want to buy one, you can look at one free in the library. There are also plenty of free papers pushed through the letterboxes these days.

Don't forget to have some paper and a pen handy to write down any jobs you find which you want to apply for.

Some of the national newspapers such as the Daily Mirror or The Sun also have job advertisement pages, but these probably won't be near where you live. If you want to leave home, you can look at these. Some of these jobs may give you somewhere to live as well.

For most jobs you will have to find somewhere to live yourself. Read the advertisements carefully so that you know what you are applying for. There are also specialist magazines such as Nursery World and Community Care Magazine for caring type jobs.

NOTICEBOARDS

There are notice boards in all colleges, and these often have job offers on them. Child care and summer jobs are usually the most common, but others do appear. This source is less likely to be available if you are attending a school. If you go out on placements or observational visits to care settings, there are often jobs advertised on the notice boards there, too. Shop windows have boards for postcards with things to sell, caravans to let, and for local jobs. Don't forget to look at them as well.

You could find child care jobs, or jobs looking after older people advertised here, and they will probably be quite near to where you live.

JOB CENTRES

Another good place to find out about work is at a Job Centre. There is one of these in each town. You should find out where the nearest one is today, somebody at your school or college will know. You can go in every day and look at the cards displayed to see if there is anything you would be interested in. You can also speak to an adviser if you want some help. They can put your name on a list, and let you know if any types of jobs you want to know about come in.

Careers Centres can do much the same thing for younger job applicants. For general advice, there may be a careers adviser in your school or college. If there is not, they should be able to make an appointment for you with one in the area.

If you are more interested in indirect work, you may be looking at advertisements for domestic staff, cooks, laundry workers, drivers, maintenance staff, etc.

AGENCIES

Employment agencies are another good source of jobs. It can be useful to use these when you cannot fit a regular work pattern into your life; you tell them when you will be available for work. They are also a good way of trying out jobs to see if you really want a permanent job as a carer, or catering assistant, or whatever.

Some agencies are general, others only do one thing, such as Home Care or Nursing

Paragon Homecall

Home Nursing Services & Nursing Agency
Want to be a
CARE ASSISTANT?
No experience - No problem!
★ We will train you.
★ Join our 5 day Course.
★ Placement usually within 20 mile radius of:
Altrincham, Crewe, Knutsford, Macclesfield,
Manchester, Salford & Stockport.
For further details 9am - 5pm, call us FREE

E0553132

CARE HOME MANAGER

For new 6-bed Home for Adults with learning difficulties.
Must have City & Guilds 325/2 qualification and
minimum 2 years' experience.
References will be required.
Salary negotiable.
Please send CV

Assistant
Manager

Adult Training
Centre

**£16,248-
£17,325
pa**

*for 37 hours per
week*

This centre offers a range of activities to 50
adults with learning disabilities, which
includes a special care facility for 12
people. You will help the Manager to lead a
committed staff team who will enable
service users to maximise their potential
and independence and will develop a
service that is responsive and sensitive to
the needs of adults with learning
disabilities and their carers.
You will preferably have a recognised
qualification (CSS, CQSW, DipSW, TMHA)
however, holders of RNMH will be
considered if you have at least two years'
experience of working at a senior level in
an Adult Training Centre. Administration
and budgeting skills, combined with
interpersonal skills and the ability to
links with other agencies in the

**Could you help Share
the Care?**

We need caring, responsible people who can welcome a child with a
disability into their home for regular short stays and who can work in
partnership with parents.
You need lots of energy, understanding and a sense of fun! You can
be any age, single or a couple, with or without children of your own.
We give you training and support and pay you a daily allowance of
£17.00.

Get in touch with Lorna to find out more.

Share the Care

Residential Care
Home for the Elderly
requires
**PART-TIME
NIGHT CARE
ATTENDANT**
No experience
necessary. Must
be reliable.

Queenscourt
Residential/
Nursing Home
have vacancies for
**Part Time RGN's
and EN's**
to work two days per
week on a rota basis
(days only) Friendly
atmosphere. Good rates
of pay
Write or telephone

Paragon Homecall

Home Nursing Services & Agency

**QUALIFIED NURSES - UPDATE
YOUR SKILLS**

if you are an RGN or an EGN who would like to return to
work, we can help update your skills to enable you to
work hours to suit you:
Phone & Transport essential, for further details -

Call us FREE on:

0800

Reg D.O.E.
No. L710

Registered with
local authorities.

E0552620

PROJECT CO-ORDINATOR/SUPPORT WORKER
Salary £13,000-£16,000 pa 37.5 h.p.w.
This innovative project provides accommodation and
continuing support for young single homeless people. The
successful applicant will lead a small highly motivated staff
team. Experience in the field is essential.

Figure 82   *Different types of job advertisement for careers*

Agencies. Agencies are a bit like Job Centres, but they are private rather than Government office. There are a lot of these around the towns and cities, but fewer in the countryside. They need people to work on what are often short term contracts looking after people in their own homes, or sometimes in Nursing Homes, Old Peoples Homes or Hospitals where they are short of regular staff. There are also agencies which specialise in finding work for nannies and nursery nurses, and you do not always need a qualification.

DIRECT CONTACT

You could also ask anyone that you know who works in health and social care if they know of any jobs you might be able to apply for.

There is nothing to stop you getting in touch with any places that you know of and asking if there is a vacancy for you. So a letter or phone call to your local hospital, Old Peoples Homes or Nursery could get you work. If you go out on placements, or have been on placements as a part of your GNVQ, you can ask the people there about job opportunities.

THE INTERNET

Searching the Internet is another good way to look for jobs. You can use it to search for jobs of the kind you want in the area you want, or put your details in and let it search for you. Find out where you can use the Internet in your school or college, and see what you can find.

Training opportunities

The school or college you are already attending ifs the best place to start asking about Training Courses, and the Careers Guidance person is the best place to start. If the infor-mation you want is not available in the college or school, then an appointment with a Careers Centre Adviser may be what you should be asking for. Don't forget to see what you can find on the Internet as well.

As well as courses at colleges, there are private companies which run training in Health and Social Care. They may also be able to get the money to pay for your training from a Government scheme.

What you need to ask about are National Traineeships and Modern Apprenticeships in Early Years work or in Health and Social Care. You will have to do a National Vocational Qualification (NVQ) in either Early Years or Care, and Key Skills at the same time. Some employers will train you for the NVQ without the key skills.

Choosing suitable jobs or training

The steps you can take to find out about suitable jobs or training in health and social care are:

- talk to your teachers/lecturers and a careers adviser
- use CD ROM's, the Internet, books and magazines in the library
- visit a careers or job centre
- use your personal contacts to get information.
- get work experience, either on placements for the course, or as a volunteer or possibly a weekend worker.

But what happens next?

Applying for jobs

After you have found the job you are interested in, what do you do next? Read the advertisement, if that is how you found out about it. It may say to write in or to telephone for an application form. It may say that you should send in your CV with a letter saying why you are interested in the job.

More often than not you will let them know that you are interested by phone or by letter, and they will send you an application form to fill in.

Fill it in the best way you can; (this will also give you evidence toward Communication Key Skills) you may be able to send your CV off with it if you are asked about your background and interests.

It is a good idea to take a photocopy of application forms before you fill them in, and use this spare copy for practice (or write in pencil so that you can rub out mistakes), and to keep for yourself when you send the real one off in the post. Make sure you send everything off by the date it says in the advertisement, or on the letter or application form.

Once the place advertising the job has all the applications in, they will decide who to invite for an interview. What you have to put on your application form helps them to decide whether to invite you or not.

Job interviews

If you are one of the few people invited to go for an interview, you know that the information you put on to your application form or into your CV got you there. So what do you need to do to prepare for a job interview?

Firstly, you should read through all the information you have available. The advertisement you first saw, the letter and job description that came with the application form, and any information you have had over the telephone or from other people who work there, if you have spoken to any.

Secondly, it is a good idea to go to the place where you will be interviewed, and to the place where you will be working (if it is different) to check how to get there, and how long it will take you.

Thirdly, think about the questions you are likely to be asked, and what your answers are going to be. You should also think about any questions that you want to ask them. It is a good idea to write these down on a piece of paper, and keep it in your pocket. You will be nervous when you are interviewed, and may not remember what you were going to ask without your note to remind you. Don't just ask about the money or the holidays as this gives a bad impression.

Finally, decide what you are going to wear. Remember that you are not going to a disco or to college, but to a job interview where you will want to make a good impression. There are usually 2 or 3 people on an interview panel, it will rarely be you with just one other person.

Some common questions

Job interviews normally start with a few words about how you are, how was your journey, the weather, and so on. When you get to the real business, there are certain questions that have to be asked, but not always in the same way. Some of these are:

- Why have you applied for this job?
- Have you any experience of this kind of work?
- Tell us about what qualifications you have (or what course you are on.)
- What qualities and skills do you have that would help you in this job?
- What sort of things are you good at (sometimes also What are your worst subjects at school or college?)

C O N F I D E N T I A L

WOLVERHAMPTON COUNCIL

APPLICATION FORM - LOCAL GOVERNMENT EMPLOYEES

Please complete this form accurately and in full as it forms the initial stage in the selection procedure.
C.V.'s will only be accepted **IN SUPPORT** of this completed form, not in place of it.

The information given on this form will be subject to **Data Protection Legislation.**

APPLICATION FOR APPOINTMENT AS:

DEPARTMENT **SOCIAL SERVICES**	POST/JOB REFERENCE NO

I. PERSONAL DETAILS

SURNAME	INITIAL(S) OF OTHER NAME(S)
ADDRESS	TEL. NUMBER HOME: WORK:
	HAVE YOU A FULL CURRENT DRIVING LICENCE ? **YES / NO** IF HGV STATE CLASS .... Answer only if relevant to mobility requirements of the post/job, or if car allowance applicable
POST CODE	

DO YOU CONSIDER YOURSELF TO BE A DISABLED PERSON? (See enclosure for more information)   **YES / NO**

People with disabilities who meet the essential job criteria will be guaranteed an interview.

DO YOU REQUIRE ANY SUPPORT OR ADJUSTMENTS TO ENABLE YOU TO TAKE PART IN THE SELECTION PROCESS
OR CARRY OUT THE DUTIES OF THE POST?   **YES / NO**
Please give details

2. EDUCATION/TRAINING/QUALIFICATIONS (include Government Training Schemes e.g. YT, if appropriate)

SCHOOL/COLLEGE/ UNIVERSITY/PLACEMENT	DATES FROM	TO	COURSES TAKEN/ QUALIFICATIONS	GRADE	DATE
MEMBERSHIP OF PROFESSIONAL BODIES					

PO 119 7/96

Figure 83   *Job application form*

Responsibilities of Care Assistant (Level 2)

1. **Organisational:**
   - The position of Care Assistant is responsible to the Manager, with functional line responsibility via the Senior Carers.

2. **Location:**
   - The position will be based at ****

3. **Purpose of Position:**
   - To work with other staff, in meeting the personal care needs of the client, in a way that respects and promotes the privacy, dignity, independence, choice, rights and personal fulfilment of each individual. To assist in enhancing the quality of life for clients by valuing each individual's uniqueness and empowering him or her to take control over their own life decisions.
   - As Care Assistants to support the Senior Care Staff and Management of the Home in helping to care for the Clients' physical environment and in the general day to day activities of the Home.

4. **Functional Responsibilities:**

   A. Personal Care:
   Assist the Client with his/her personal care needs, consistent with the supervision provided within the establishment. This will include:

   - Assisting a client who may need help with dressing, undressing, bathing and the toilet.
   - Helping clients with mobility problems or other physical difficulties, including the promotion of continence, help in the use of aids and personal equipment.
   - Caring for a client who is unwell.
   - Helping to care for a client who is dying.
   - Assist in the promotion of mental and physical stimulation for users through active listening, conversation, sharing in activities such as reading, writing, hobbies and other recreational pursuits, together with escort duties as directed.
   - Support those who need assistance to eat or drink.
   - Make and change beds as appropriate, tidy rooms and undertake the appropriate amount of light cleaning.
   - Empty and clean commodes as necessary.
   - Participate in the laundering function of the Home as appropriate.
   - Assist with the setting of trays and tables and in the serving of meals.
   - Help with the preparation of meals and with the washing up as appropriate.
   - Assist with tidying and clearing dining areas and trays.
   - Answering emergency bells, the door and the telephone, dealing with such calls in a polite and professional manner, passing on the information in the appropriate manner.

Figure 84   *A job description for a Care Assistant*

Figure 85   *Interviews are normally carried out by a panel*

- Questions about the job, and what you may do in certain situations:

  e.g. 'If you found Mrs Smith had fallen out of bed, what would you do?'

  'We have a no smoking policy in this building; if Mr Jones wanted a smoke, how would you deal with it?'
- How will you manage with getting here for 8a.m./working shifts/working nights?
- Have you any questions you would like to ask us?

Sometimes straight after an interview you will be told whether you have got the job or not. Usually you will have to wait a while, as there will be more people to interview after you. Then you may have either a phone call or a letter (sometimes both) to tell you if you have got the job or not.

Student exercise

Use the job description printed earlier and get everybody in your group to apply for it. In two groups, go through the applications and see who you would invite to an interview.

- For those who did not get invited, tell them why (in writing), and get them to apply again.
- Group A will look at the applications from Group B, and Group B will look at the applications from Group A.
- When all the applications are satisfactory, set up your own interview panels of three people each, and interview the job

applicants from the other group. Make sure that everybody has a turn on the interview panel, and that everybody is interviewed.

- Taking part in the interview will give you evidence towards Key Skills in Communication.
- After the interview, the panel should give feedback to the person they have just interviewed. Did they come across well? Have they given them the job? Did they answer the questions clearly and fully? How could they do better?

TUTOR EXERCISE

An alternative to peer interviews is to arrange more formal interviews using teaching staff, or outsiders form the local Lions Club, Chamber of Commerce, or something similar.

An important element of any of the interviews is to have written feedback which can be included in portfolios.

CURRICULUM VITAE

Don't let words put you off; a curriculum vitae, or CV is just a record of your life so far. If you have been keeping a Record of Achievement (ROA), or a progress file from school, this can be a part of your CV.

The difference between a CV and a life story is that in a CV you pick out the parts that are important for a particular purpose. So if you are applying for a job working with children, you concentrate on your experience of looking after children. This may be babysitting, or looking after your own younger brothers and sisters, or any job you might have had – whether it was paid or not – where you were looking after children. You will need a CV because many employers will ask you for one whenever you apply for a job.

Putting a CV together

Student activity

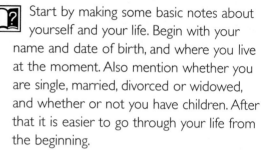 Start by making some basic notes about yourself and your life. Begin with your name and date of birth, and where you live at the moment. Also mention whether you are single, married, divorced or widowed, and whether or not you have children. After that it is easier to go through your life from the beginning.

- Write down a few notes about your family; who is in it? Have you any brothers or sisters? Are they older or younger than you?
- Can you remember if you went to any playgroups or nurseries?
- Which primary and junior schools did you go to?
- Which secondary schools did you attend?
- Did you pass any exams there (GCSEs, A Levels, or any other)?
- Have you had any jobs? Think of Saturday jobs, evening jobs, newspaper rounds, babysitting, or anything else whether it was paid or unpaid.
- What are you good at?
- What don't you like doing?
- Are you in, or have you ever been in any clubs or groups such as Scouts, Guides, Brownies, Cubs, Churches, Youth clubs, Athletics clubs, Swimming clubs, etc?
- What are your hobbies? What do you do in your spare time?
- What are you studying or working at now?
- What would you like to do next?
- And after that?

These notes can now be used to write a proper CV which you can keep up to date, and use whenever you apply for a job, or perhaps another course.

The real thing

If possible, keep your CV on a computer disk, as it is easier to change it when you need to, and print off as many as you need without all the hard work of writing it out again and again. This will also give you evidence towards Key Skills in Information Technology.

When you are writing out the final version of your CV, using a lot of different headings makes it easier for you to write, and easier for other people to read. These are some suggested headings which should be OK for most things, but you may need to put some others in or leave things out depending on what you are going to use the CV for.

Always start with the basic information:

FULL NAME
ADDRESS & telephone number
DATE OF BIRTH
NATIONALITY AND THE TOWN WHERE YOU WERE BORN
MARITAL STATUS (As we have said above, this is whether you are single, married, divorced, living with someone, widowed, and whether you have children or not.)

EDUCATION RECORD. Put down here all the schools you have been to, and the dates when you started and when you left.

QUALIFICATIONS. Leave this out if you have none, or put in any GCSE's, City & Guilds, BTEC or any other qualifications you have, and the year that you got them.

AWARDS. If you have any awards for swimming, athletics, playing a musical instrument, or for bravery, or Duke of Edinburgh's awards, etc., then mention them here.

EMPLOYMENT RECORD. Put here any jobs you have had, and the dates when you started and when you finished.

CURRENT EMPLOYMENT. Only to be used when you actually have a job at the time of writing, it may be part-time or full-time, paid or voluntary.

HOBBIES AND INTERESTS. Put down here what you do in your own time.

REFEREES. When you apply for jobs, and sometimes for courses, you will be asked to give the names and addresses of two referees who know you. One should know you from works, school or college, the other can be a friend. Always ask them if it is alright to put their names down as referees.

Here is an example of how a completed Curriculum Vitae may look:

CURRICULUM VITAE FOR J. SHIELDS.

FULL NAME: JENNIFER ANNE SHIELDS
ADDRESS: 16 WENTWORTH CLOSE
                  LESTALL
                  WENNOCKSHIRE
                  ZS2 9US
TELEPHONE: 01836 923814
DATE OF BIRTH: 25.1.80

NATIONALITY: ENGLISH; BORN IN SEALFORD, NEAR TOLCHESTER.
MARITAL STATUS: SINGLE, NO CHILDREN.

EDUCATION   LOCKTON ST. PRIMARY SCHOOL, SEALFORD 1984 – 1987
RECORD: LESTALL JUNIOR SCHOOL 1987 – 91
                  HEELBY COMPREHENSIVE SCHOOL 1991 – 96
                  HEELBY COLLEGE OF FURTHER EDUCATION 1996 –

QUALIFICATIONS: GCSE'S IN ENGLISH GRADE C
                  MATHS GRADE D
                  HOME ECONOMICS GRADE B

AWARDS: FIRST AID CERTIFICATE FROM RED CROSS
                  LIFESAVERS BADGE FROM SWIMMING
                  BAGA AWARD FOR GYMNASTICS
                  BALLET CERTIFICATE

EMPLOYMENT: NEWSPAPER DELIVERIES 1992-3
                  FRUIT PICKING IN SUMMER HOLIDAYS
                  BABYSITTING FOR PEOPLE NEAR WHERE I LIVE
                  WAITRESS IN LESTALL ARMS PUB 1995 – NOW

HOBBIES AND INTERESTS: SPORTS (IN NETBALL AND ROUNDERS TEAMS)
                  GOING TO DISCOS
                  WATCHING TV AND VIDEOS
                  HELPING AT BROWNIES

REFEREES: MR. M. WINTON   MISS T. HALL
            HEELBY COMPREHENSIVE   BRIAR PATCH
            HEELBY   LESTALL LANE
            WENNOCKSHIRE   LESTALL
            HL6 5MN   WENNOCKSHIRE
                                       ZS2 9YG

Student exercise

To help you think about what you are good at, and what you may need some help with, answer the following questions by ticking the one which you think most applies to you.

Listening and Attending	Tick a box
1. I am very good at listening to others and usually give them my full attention.	
2. I can listen fairly well but I am easily distracted.	
3. I find listening to people difficult and prefer talking.	
4. I am not very good at listening at all.	

Talking: Giving Information	Tick a box
1. I usually give appropriate and clear information.	
2. I give as much information as possible whenever I can.	
3. I like to assess what information people want before I offer it.	
4. I don't particularly like giving information to people.	

Talking: Supporting	Tick a box
1. I am usually very supportive of other people.	
2. I can support people but have my limits.	
3. I prefer other people to be supportive.	
4. Trying to be supportive makes me anxious and I am not very good at it.	

Talking: Drawing Out	Tick a box
1. I can draw people out fairly easily and enjoy doing it.	
2. I can sometimes draw people out but I don't often achieve it.	
3. I find drawing people out difficult.	
4. I try to avoid drawing people out.	

Talking: Confronting	Tick a box
1. I can confront effectively when I need to.	
2. I tend to be more aggressive than confronting.	
3. I tend to be more submissive than confronting.	
4. I don't like confronting people at all.	

Talking: Coping with Emotions	Tick a box
1. I cope with other peoples' emotion well.	
2. I can cope if someone cries but I don't feel very comfortable.	
3. I would call someone to help if someone started to cry.	
4. I do not like coping with other peoples' emotions at all.	

Opening a Conversation	Tick a box
1. I can start conversations very easily.	
2. I can start a conversation with some difficulty.	
3. I try to let the other person start the conversation.	
4. I find the whole topic very difficult.	

Structuring a Conversation	Tick a box
1. I find it very easy to control and structure a conversation.	
2. I do not normally think about structuring.	
3. I usually leave the structuring of a conversation to the other person.	
4. I prefer to be 'natural' in a conversation.	

Ending a Conversation	Tick a box
1. I can usually end a conversation quite easily.	
2. I often find it difficult to end conversations.	
3. I usually wait till the other person finishes the conversation.	
4. I find ending conversations very difficult.	

Working in Groups	Tick a box
1. I enjoy group work and find no difficulty in working with groups.	
2. I am sometimes unsure what to say in group meetings.	
3. I would rather not work in groups.	
4. I try to avoid groups.	

Running Groups	Tick a box
1. I would enjoy chairing or facilitating a group meeting.	
2. I think I could run a group if I was asked to.	
3. I would feel very uncomfortable if I was asked to run a group.	
4. I could not run a group.	

Being Assertive	**Tick a box**
1. I think I am assertive.	
2. I am more aggressive than assertive.	
3. I am more submissive that assertive.	
4. I am not sure whether or not I am assertive.	

Writing Skills	**Tick a box**
1. I write fairly clearly and well.	
2. I need to improve my writing skills.	
3. I do not write well.	
4. I try to avoid putting things in writing.	

Computing Skills	**Tick a box**
1. I am quite happy using computers of different sorts.	
2. I can use a computer but not very easily.	
3. I don't know much about computers.	
4. I avoid computers if possible.	

Self-Awareness	**Tick a box**
1. I think I know myself reasonably well.	
2. I need to get to know myself better.	
3. I am often surprised by the things that I do.	
4. I don't think I know myself at all.	

Self-check questions

1 What do the letters CV stand for?
2 What will you need a CV for?
3 How should you start putting a CV together?
4 Why is it best to keep your CV on a computer disk?
5 Why is it worth considering voluntary jobs?
6 Name an organisation that will help you with information about voluntary jobs.
7 Name 3 places where you can find out about jobs in Health & Social care.
8 Why should you copy job application forms?
9 Write down two things you should do before going for a job interview.
10 What are two questions commonly asked at job interviews?

Letter of application

When you send off your CV, you should also include with it a letter of application, unless there is an Application Form to fill in.

This should tell the person what job you are interested in, where you heard about it, and that you have enclosed a CV.

Portfolio

Remember what you need for your portfolio:

- A description of how you found out about the job or training course that you applied for

- Background information on the job or training you want to do
- A record of your job interview
- A copy of your completed application form and the letter you wrote to send off for it
- A review of the whole process of applying

ASSESSMENT EVIDENCE

You need to produce an employment folder which includes:

• information about the main ways to find out about jobs or training

• information about jobs or training that interest you

• an application for a job or training of your choice which must include a letter and your CV or a letter and a completed application form

• a record of your performance in a mock interview

To achieve a pass you must show you can:	To achieve a merit you must also show you can:	To achieve a distinction you must also show you can:
• use appropriate information to find out about a job or training vacancy that interests you	• find and use relevant information about jobs or training that interest you, using a source not provided for you	• present your application in an effective and suitable manner, convincingly showing the links between your interests and experience and the job
• provide relevant information in your written application for the job or training place	• explain clearly in your written application why you are suitable for the job you have chosen	• thoroughly review your information search, application and interview, identifying ways to improve your job-seeking skills
• answer an interviewer's questions clearly and carefully	• use appropriate non-verbal and verbal skills to communicate your interest during an interview	

C H A P T E R 9

Working as part of a team

CONTENTS AND LINKS

Whenever and wherever you may work in health and social care, you will usually be a part of a team. The team may not always be there at the same time, but it is still a team. Home carers (Home Helps), for example, work individually in their clients' homes, but they are still part of a home care team. It is the same in hospitals; the night staff are still a part of the caring team, even if they only meet the day staff for a short period at the beginning and end of shifts.

So being able to work as part of a team is important; there will always be times when you have to rely on other people, and when other people are relying on you. How would your teachers/lecturers and yourselves manage if the college was not kept clean, warm and tidy; if the equipment was not there and in working order when it was needed? It is just the same working in health and social care settings. A team of people working together is needed to provide any of the services required.

In this unit you will learn about the following aspects of teamwork:

- choosing an activity and identifying the aims
- planning a team activity, identifying the roles and responsibilities of team members
- carrying out an activity
- reviewing an activity to find out how the team worked

Work for this unit will also give you evidence for the Key Skill unit 'Working with others'.

Choosing an activity and identifying the aims

The first thing that you will have to do is decide what activity you want to be involved in. Next you should check that you and all the other members of the team understand what you want to get from the activity.

The team will then have to agree on what needs to be done.

Start by looking at what is available for you to use. These are known as the resources, and include such things as how many people there are, what rooms or fields you could use, how much time you have, and how much money you can get, plus anything else that you may need to use. Make sure that every team member takes part in this discussion.

The next important job is to decide who will be doing what, and that everybody has something to do.

You should also look at what might go wrong, and how the team will deal with any problems. The team will also have to make sure that nobody is in any danger at any time. If you are to use any equipment, make sure that you know how to use it properly. Do not stand on chairs or window-sills; get a pair of stepladders. If your activity is to be outside at night, wear reflective clothing. Look closely at what you decide to do, and think of the safety measures which need to be taken.

The best way to do all this is to hold a meeting, and elect one of your group to be a chairperson, and another to keep a written record of what has been decided. Enough copies of this record need to be made for everybody to have one to keep in their file. Using a computer disk makes this a much easier job, and gives the writer evidence toward their key skills in Information technology and Communication.

Each member of the team should also keep a record of your own part in the planning process, and what contributions they have made.

At the end of this section, you should have records for your portfolio which show that you have:

1 Checked that you have an accurate understanding of the aims of the activity.

2 Agreed actions which will meet these aims.
3 Contributed to identifying the resources which are available.
4 Contributed to identifying which team members are going to carry out different parts of the activity.
5 Contributed to identifying actions to deal with possible problems and maintain health and safety.
6 Contributed to producing a realistic team plan for the overall activity.
7 Agreed and produced a realistic individual plan which provides details of your own role in the activity.

One of the easiest ways to do this is to keep a notebook, and jot down in it what you have done and agreed to do next after each meeting, or after each piece of work involved with the activity.

Ideas for activities

- So what sort of team activities can you do in Health and Social Care?
- What about organising a party? This may be for children under eight years old, and could be a Christmas, Easter, Halloween, or birthday party.
- It could be a party or a lunch for older people at a Day Centre or Social Club, or an entertainment of some sort for those living in a residential home.
- Perhaps a party for people with learning difficulties who attend your college?
- Or even a party or disco for yourselves at the end of term, or for Christmas – or the end of the course?

Aims

So what are the aims of the activity you have chosen going to be? That is, what do you want to do? Make people happy, take them out, teach them something they did not know before? At the very least, a safe and successful activity; and one which gives you the evidence to achieve this unit.

Actions

What will the team have to do to organise the activity?

Having decided what the activity will be, and who it will be for, you will next need to decide when and where, and then get permission for that. This can only be done when you know the details. If it is at the school or college, you will need to get permission from there. If it is to be somewhere else, you will have to find out whom you should be contacting.

- How much money will you need?
- Where will it come from?
- Will you have to pay to use the room?
- What other things will you need to get?

Make a list divided into what you need to buy and what you can borrow or get for free. Invitations and envelopes need to be on the list, and posters to advertise your activity. Designing and making posters will give you evidence for your key skills.

Food and drinks, plates, cups, tablecloths – will you need knives, forks and spoons; or will you be serving sandwiches and cakes which people can eat with their fingers? What about rubbish bags and things for cleaning up afterwards? Will you need equipment for any games to be played? Who is going to be doing what?

These are only ideas to get you started. You will have to discuss the details of what you are going to do and what you think you will need with your teacher or lecturer.

Another idea is to organise an outing. This can be for the same types of group mentioned before (children, older people, people with learning difficulties). Decide who to invite, and then where you would like to take them. Then you will have to sort out the days when it is suitable for everybody concerned. Some points to consider are:

- which day of the week would be most suitable
- the times of the day for the outing to begin or end
- the distance to be travelled and how long it will take
- how you will get everybody there and back (walking, in cars, on the train, on a bus)
- how much it is all going to cost
- where the money is going to come from
- what arrangements need to be made for food (does anybody need a special diet)
- does anybody need to take medicines.

Once again, these are only ideas to start you off.

You might need to do some fundraising to raise money for your activity, and this can give you evidence for teamworking as well.

Your activity could be fundraising for a voluntary organisation, as they always need money. They will also give you lots of advice and guidance on how it should be done.

One voluntary organisation which organises holidays for disabled people is the Winged Fellowship Trust (Angel House, 20-32 Pentonville Rd, London N1 9XD).

The guidelines below are reproduced with their kind permission:

HOW TO ORGANISE A FUNDRAISING EVENT

Considerations

1   <u>Previous experience</u>
Have you ever run a similar event before. If not, and you know of anyone who has, it may be useful to ask their advice.

2   <u>Steps to take?</u>
What steps do you need to take to run the event? It is always helpful to make a plan, with dates. For example, if running a quiz and buffet evening, the steps might be

<u>Step</u>	<u>Date</u>
Decide on a date and get some friends committed to help you on the day!	
Organise venue/time etc.	23 October
Get tickets printed	25 October
Send out tickets for selling	1 November
Publicise the event	2 November
Ring round to check numbers	26 November
Buy provisions	28 November
Organise tables, chairs etc.	29 November
Brief everyone helping at event	30 November

3   <u>Can you run the event on your own?</u>

If not, you need to gather together a group of helpers and give them all specific tasks so that they know exactly what they are expected to do. Find out their interests and talents and maximise them as much as possible, as people enjoy doing things they are good at or interested in.

4   <u>Budget</u>

<u>*Budget checklist*</u>   It is useful to work out how much you will have to spend when running an event. You could use this sheet as a checklist and jot down how much each item will cost. This might include

<u>*Printing*</u>
Tickets
Sponsor forms
Leaflets
Posters
Invitations

<u>*Photography*</u>
Films
Batteries

Provisions
Food
Drink

Hire of equipment
Chairs/tables
Room hire
Video
Public announcement system

Prizes
Raffles or other (if possible get as many prizes donated as you can)

However, many events are put on specifically for the purpose of publicity and therefore whatever is raised is a bonus. It is important to keep costs to a minimum and if you can manage to get anything sponsored or donated this will help the overall profit potential of the event.

5   Tickets and sponsor forms

If it is a ticketed or sponsored event make sure that tickets are sold and sponsor forms sent out well in advance. Be sure that the legal requirements are complied with. If in doubt, ask someone who works for the charity you are fundraising for, or your local police, as they will be able to advise you.

6   Publicity

You can get lists of local media contacts from your local library, e.g. radio, local papers, local 'what's on' publications.

Special considerations

Make sure that whatever you do is
    A)   safe
    B)   legal
    C)   cost effective
    D)   fun!!

Figure 86   *Organising a fundraising event – guidelines from the Winged Fellowship Trust*

Apart from going round with a collecting tin asking people for money, there are many sponsored activities which can be done as a team, e.g. sponsored walks, clean-ups, horserides, swims, pancake races and so on. Decide who you want to raise money for, make contact with them, and ask for their advice and guidance. They may even send someone to speak to you and help you with the activity.

Even visits you do as a part of the course can be organised as a team activity; such things as arranging visits to a hospital, a special school or a residential home. Going to a careers convention – or organising it yourself and inviting other students.

For any activity that you decide to organise, you will need to stick to the dates and deadlines you have decided upon, and make changes if things do not go exactly as planned. Don't forget to keep a record of all this for your portfolio.

Cookery activity

One activity which can be done in most schools and colleges is to cook a meal together, as a team exercise. This could be linked in any work you are doing for Unit 5 (Planning Diets).

- Decide what the meal is going to be
- Decide when the meal is going to be
- How many people will be eating?
- Keep a record of what your tasks will be

- How much is it going to cost?
- How much will that be for each person?
- Where is the money coming from?
- What pots and pans will you need? Are they all easily available?
- Who is going to do the shopping?
- Make sure that you know all the health and safety rules of the kitchen you will be using.

What can go wrong?

If you have decided upon an outdoor event, the weather may not be good. Make plans to cover this, either to use an indoor place or change the activity to one that can be held indoors; possibly even a plan in reserve to change the date.

Think about problems that could happen, like people turning up late or not turning up

Figure 87   *Plan for what can go wrong*

at all; transport breaking down, and people getting injured. Have a plan ready so that everybody knows what to do if it happens.

If at all possible, it is a good idea to video the activity. You can then use the video both as portfolio evidence, key skills evidence, and to help you review the activity after it is all over. For some things, an audio tape may be OK to use as a record.

In order to build up the evidence you need for your portfolio, you will need to show that you have:

1 followed the activities in the agreed individual plan and the agreed team plan.
2 Made the best use of available resources.
3 Maintained health and safety.
4 Co-operated effectively with others as required by the plans.
5 Responded to problems promptly and in the correct way.

You will need a copy of the overall plan which was completed by the person elected to keep notes for you during the meetings when everything was being planned. If you were that person, you should make sure that everybody has a copy and agrees with what you have put in it.

When it was decided who would be doing what to help toward the event, that is your individual plan. You should make sure that you write down what you have agreed to do, and how you are going to do it. So if you are going to make phone calls and write letters, you should plan in advance who you are going to telephone and write to, and what, and when. If you have to book a room, for instance, it is no good inviting anybody until you know if it is free when you want it. So the order in which things have to be done is an important part of planning.

Explain why you have done things the way you have, and why this was the best way to use your time and other resources.

Explain how you will make sure everybody is safe, both for your part in the activity and the activity as a whole.

Write something about how you worked with the other members of the team, and how you decided who would be doing what.

Also keep a record of how you dealt with any problems that came up, and who you worked with to deal with them. Remember to record any key skills which you have used.

As a part of the evidence, you will need to have one of the tutors/teachers observing what you are doing toward this activity. Find out which member of staff it is, and that they know your plan of action, and plans to deal with any problems, before you start.

If you are going to take any videos, photographs or tape-recordings, check that you have everything you need, including spare film and tapes, and that the equipment is working properly.

Evidence of teamworking

Your portfolio evidence will need to show that you have:

- communicated with other team members using verbal, non-verbal and listening skills
- understood and worked to the team aims
- supported team members by providing helpful feedback
- knew when you or your team needed help and contacted the appropriate person
- kept team members informed of problems and solutions
- carried out your role in accordance with the plan.

Reviewing the activity

Now that all the excitement and enjoyment of the activity is over, it is time to look at how things went; so you will have to:

1 Review the extent to which the overall aims were met.
2 Review the use of resources.
3 Review whether responses to problems worked.
4 Review maintenance of health and safety.
5 Provide clear and constructive feedback to others on their performance.
6 Respond constructively to feedback from others.
7 Make and record suggestions for improvements in the way similar activities are tackled in the future.

If you were able to take a video of the activity, you can use this as an aid to reviewing it now.

The questions you should be asking are such things as:

- Did I do what I said I would do?
- Did I manage to do it in the way I set out to do it?
- Were the other members of the team doing what they said they would do?
- Did the team achieve its' goals?
- Did each member of it achieve their goal?

The team should discuss this as a group – without anybody getting too angry, and look at each others performance. If there is any praise to be given, then give it. If some criticism is needed, then make it constructive criticism, including looking at reasons why something was or was not done, and how things could be changed to avoid these problems next time.

Were people given the tasks most suited to their abilities and interests?

Was the equipment and materials used the most appropriate, and was it used in the best way?

How long did the whole thing take; could this time be reduced, or was more needed? Why?

How did the exercise seem to the observers, your teacher or lecturer?

Make sure that you get their views on the assignment as a whole, and on your individual performance.

Was it a safe exercise? Were all the Health & Safety requirements taken into account?

Did any accidents happen? Why? How were they dealt with?

Write, tape-record or video a short piece for your portfolio on how you think you would do things differently if you could do this activity again, including comments on all the points mentioned above.

At the end of these discussions, you should be able to identify

- what went well
- what did not go well
- how well you carried out your role
- how well your team members worked as a team
- how you and your team could have worked together better
- how teamwork helped the activity

AND have the evidence to prove it in your portfolio.

ASSESSMENT EVIDENCE

You need to produce a record of a team activity and your involvement. It should include:

- details of the activity and its aims
- a plan for the activity
- a record of the activity that identifies what you did as well as what other team members did
- a review of your role in the activity and how the team worked as a whole

To achieve a pass you must show you can:	To achieve a merit you must also show you can:	To achieve a distinction you must also show you can:
• clearly describe the team activity and its aims	• plan and carry out your role effectively to meet agreed deadlines	• identify possible problems with the plan and work out ways for the team to avoid them
• work co-operatively with your team to draw up a realistic plan that includes: – a list of tasks and who will do them – realistic deadlines – resources needed	• use your communication skills well in order to be an effective team member	• use your communication skills effectively to improve other team members' performance
• check that the tasks are being completed on time, revising the plan if it is not working	• understand and explain: – what worked well and what did not – how well you carried out your role – how well your team members worked	• make realistic suggestions as to how you could have improved the way your team worked
• describe what you and other team members did during the activity		

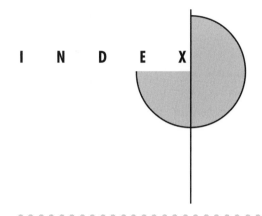

INDEX